Ageing and

Ageing and Reminiscence Processes

Social and Clinical Implications

Peter G. Coleman

Departments of Geriatric Medicine/Social Work Studies
University of Southampton

JOHN WILEY & SONS

Chichester · New York · Brisbane · Toronto · Singapore

Copyright © 1986 by John Wiley & Sons Ltd.

First published in paperback November 1989

Library of Congress Cataloging in Publication Data:

Coleman, Peter G.
  Ageing and reminiscence processes.

  Bibliography: p.
  Includes index.
  1. Reminiscing. 2. Aged—Psychology. 3. Aged—Mental
health. I. Title.
BF724.85.R45C64 1987   155.67   86-15800
ISBN 0 471 91027 9
ISBN 0 471 92639 6 pbk

British Library Cataloguing in Publication Data:

Coleman, Peter G.
  Ageing and reminiscence processes: social
  and clinical implications.
  1. Memory 2. Age and intelligence
  I. Title
  153.1′2 BF378.A/
ISBN 0 471 91027 9
ISBN 0 471 92639 6 pbk

Typeset by Witwell Ltd, Liverpool
Printed and bound in Great Britain by
Biddles Ltd, Guildford and King's Lynn

To
Maria and Leonardo,
to Mum and Dad,
and to my Grandmothers
with love.

Ce livre essentiel, le seul livre vrai, un grand écrivain n'a pas, dans le sens courant, à l'inventer, puisqu'il existe déjà en chacun de nous.

Marcel Proust

As a well spent day brings happy sleep, so life well used brings happy death.

Leonardo da Vinci

History is bunk!

Henry Ford

No man can have in his mind a conception of the future, for the future is not yet. But of our conceptions of the past, we make a future.

Thomas Hobbes

I forget the past and strain ahead for what is still to come.

St Paul

Contents

Acknowledgements

I should like to acknowledge the Social Science Research Council who funded my research studentship for three years at London University (1969–72), and the housing managers and wardens of the London boroughs concerned who facilitated the initial research study. I am grateful to staff and fellow post-graduate students at the Department of Psychology, Bedford College, London University, who supported my work, and to the stimulus and assistance provided by subsequent colleagues at the Gerontological Centre in Nijmegen, The Netherlands and at the University of Southampton.

I am particularly grateful to Dr Sheila Chown for her wise advice and supervision in the early years. I should like to express my appreciation to Mrs Valerie White for her skilful transcribing of the taped conversations, Mrs Barbara Giddins for her efficient typing of the manuscript, and Professor Malcolm Johnson and Dr Joanna Bornat for their helpful comments on an initial draft. I should also like to thank my family for the encouragement they have given me to complete this book.

I wish to express my gratitude, above all though, to the persons themselves who are the subjects of this book, for being willing to open their lives to me and for their friendship.

Chapter 1

Introduction

The last 25 years have seen an improvement in attention and respect paid to older people. This might seem an odd statement to make when we know that so much is wrong with our society's provision for old age. Yet the increasing awareness of the opportunities denied the old, and the beginnings of a sensitivity to the 'ageism' expressed often unknowingly in our thoughts, speech and action, signify changing currents. We are hopefully at the beginnings of the reversal of a historical trend of growing denigration of older people whose origin is dated by some scholars to as far back as the end of the eighteenth century (see Fischer, 1978). Donald Cowgill, who in his book *Aging and Modernization* (Cowgill and Holmes, 1972), first gave prominence to the theme that modernization as a historical process had resulted in lowering the status of older people in society, has recently acknowledged that there is now a clear trend in the opposite direction—at least in the United States. 'There has been a reversal of that trend within the United States, dating from about 1960. All social indicators show that the welfare and status of the elderly in the United States have moved upward since that time' (Cowgill, 1984, p. 225).

A greater interest in older people's reminiscences, talking and thinking about past experience, is also part of this development. Not so long ago reminiscence was one of the traits of later life that was scornfully dismissed. Now we are ready to consider what it means to the older person, and perhaps even more importantly what it can mean to us. The growing interest in oral history indicates something of this new appreciation. We seek means for ensuring that people's memories survive them. For we realize that as each generation dies, so opportunities for recovering experiences of previous life circumstances are lost for ever. This point of view now has eloquent advocates in Britain (see, for example, Paul Thompson's *The Voice of the Past: Oral History*, Thompson, 1978).

Within the study of the psychology of ageing, which is the framework for the work described in this book, attitudes to reminiscence used to be extremely negative. The reversal of these attitudes is most graphically illustrated in the career of Robert Havighurst, a developmental psychologist and one of the pioneers in the study of social and psychological processes in ageing. At the end of the 1950s he was advising older people to avoid reminiscence (Havighurst,

1

1959). A little over 10 years later he was researching the benefits of reminiscence (Havighurst and Glasser, 1972).

Like all human activities, this book has its history. How far one wants to trace back influences depends on one's enthusiasm. As a boy I know I spent a lot of time talking to my grandmothers (my grandfathers were both dead), and I enjoyed their company. I listened to them and they listened to me. I remember being disappointed by the lack of attention to issues related to ageing within the psychology degree course I followed at university—the situation within UK psychology departments is little better today. When I was given the opportunity to carry out post-graduate research in psychology in 1969, the field of ageing presented itself as a natural choice, and reminiscence seemed to me an ideal subject for enquiry. History had been the subject which fascinated me most at school, and I would speak about nineteenth and twentieth century history with my grandmothers. I can remember one occasion when I read out loud to them Barbara Tuchman's graphic description of King Edward VII's funeral procession in her book on the origins of the First World War, and how that procession symbolized a world that was about to disappear for ever. That very same procession is described by one of the people in this book, Mrs Tucker, who was there (on page 116). For as long as I can remember it has been a great enjoyment for me to look back on historical events with the perspective of time.

When I was beginning my post-graduate studies and was looking around for literature that described the important distinguishing marks of old age, I soon came across and was impressed by Robert Butler's article on reminiscence and the 'life review' (Butler, 1963). Having started on this path I found other work that is described in the following chapter. I also had the opportunity to speak to Robert Havighurst, while on a visit to London, about his own research on reminiscence, and I began to feel part of a developing crusade.

The most interesting questions about memories seem to me to relate to people's use of memories in ordinary life rather than in laboratories. Memory has always been an important subject for psychological research over the last one hundred years, but too much energy has been expended in the search for empirical generalizations in artificial experimental situations. The sophisticated models and controversies that have been the fruit of such work hardly impinge on the questions that most people have about their memory. It is only now after the impetus provided by the ethologists' emphasis on the study of animal behaviour in natural environments, that psychologists have begun to abandon their impatience to formulate general theories and to realize that their subject must be grounded more on the careful observation of naturally occurring phenomena (Neisser, 1982).

The use that old people make of their memories, then, has become a respectable subject for psychological research; the forms reminiscence takes, the circumstances on which it depends and the differences between individuals in their use of the past. Memory is much more than recall of past stimuli. It involves emotion, will and creativity in the reconstruction of the past to serve present needs. 'The mind never photographs, it paints pictures' said Pear in his classic book on memory (Pear, 1922), and the artistic function of memory has been acknowledged by a number of authors, most notably Proust. He renounced ordinary life entirely in order to achieve 'remembrance of things past', and argued that events and personal experience can only properly be understood and appreciated in retrospect, in remembrance. Indeed the recognition of the value of the study of history relies on this insight. The significance of people and events, movements and philosophies can rarely be appreciated at the time, but only in the context of a retrospective view. That view is constantly open to change the further on history moves, and the further back one looks to connect more and more events. The achieving of a perspective depends on a view from a distance.

The power of memory in providing direction to life indeed has long been celebrated. In Greek mythology Mnemosyne, the goddess of memory, is the mother of the Muses and hence of all art. Men have long lived according to the insight that a life lived reflectively—by a daily examination of conscience for example—is the path to a better life. To those in difficulties memories have also proved a solace, sometimes coming unsolicited to provide an unexpected strength such that 'then' becomes 'now'. In discussing her own personal experiences of recapturing childhood memories while abroad and homesick for Russia, Esther Salaman quotes Dostoyevsky: '...some people appear not to think of their memories of childhood, but all the same preserve such memories unconsciously. They may be grave, bitter, but the suffering we have lived through may turn in the end into sacred things for the soul...' (Salaman, 1970).

Yet there have been those who have warned against this same power that comes from the past in memory. There can be a conflict, it must be recognized, between the requirements from the past and present. Some have felt themselves compelled to break the bonds with the past and to create new ways of working or to begin afresh. The psychoanalyst Schachtel has written dramatically of the conflict between the delights of recollection and the demands of the present (Schachtel, 1959). Odysseus bound himself to the mast to escape the Siren's call. Such attitudes and experiences we must also be prepared to find among old people who see a task they have to fulfil.

As with any reaction after a period of neglect there is a danger of exaggeration. Reminiscence may be more important for older people than has been thought hitherto, but it is not all important. Above all we must be prepared to be sensitive to individual differences. Reminiscence may be useful to some but not to others. Experience of ageing is not uniform. Much interesting work has been carried out in the 1960s and 1970s on different lifestyles in later life, that we should be wary now of over-simple generalizations about what is good for older people (see, for example, Neugarten et al., 1964; Williams and Wirths, 1965; Maas and Kuyper, 1977, Taylor and Ford, 1981).

In the study described in this book, which I set out on 16 years ago and which has become a longitudinal study, since I have continued to visit almost every person up until their deaths, the aim from the outset has been to investigate the use to which reminiscence is put in people's lives, and more particularly how it relates to their adjustment to their present life circumstances. The key literature which shaped this enquiry is set out in the next chapter, and the ensuing two chapters describe the characteristics of the people I interviewed, their attitudes to life in general and to reminiscence in particular. The main body of the book is contained in chapters 5 to 9, which present case studies of particular individuals who demonstrated certain attitudes to reminiscence, whether of attraction or avoidance, preoccupation or indifference. Each person's attitudes are presented in relation to the evidence I collected on their state of adjustment.

I have decided on a case study method for analysis and presentation because I believe it to be the most suitable method of exploratory and descriptive research into human adjustment. As a method it has been neglected hitherto, quite unjustifiably in my opinion, in favour of research using large numbers of subjects, sophisticated statistical analysis and pre-defined questions. Yet when we only have the beginnings of an understanding of a subject as broad as adjustment, we cannot sensibly pre-define all the questions we want answers to or the variables we want to include in our analysis. We need to acquaint ourselves in depth with the relevant material. Every science has had to go through an initial descriptive period in its development, yet psychology dealing with the most complex matter of human behaviour has often tried to rush on ahead of itself. If we truly love our subject, we should be prepared to be more patient.

If case study material is to be properly exploited in psychological research on adjustment, a more rigorous methodology is required (see Bromley, 1986). Case studies provide an opportunity for deeper insight into individual situations, but also for biased presentation. Strict adherence to procedures for presenting all the relevant evidence are required. If this is done openly and any possible sources of bias acknowledged, the case study provides a rich source for scientific advancement, via the analysis of particular cases to 'types' of cases and the development of 'case-law'. The detailed study of individuals requires considerable patience on the part of the investigator and trust and co-operation on the part of the subject, but the results are immensely satisfying. The present study is a far from perfect example of case study methodology, but it is hoped that the glimpses it provides of reality may encourage others to do better.

It is also a characteristic of this book that I have chosen to lay considerable emphasis on the presentation of the subject's own views about their situation, and in their own words. The phenomenological perspective in psychology has begun to teach us to respect more individuals' own views on themselves. I have aimed to be true to George Kelly's dictum, 'if you want to know something about somebody, why not ask them'. This may not be the last word on someone. But it certainly should be the first one.

Throughout the case studies and in the concluding chapter in particular, I have tried to provide hints for helping professionals and voluntary workers in the health and social services, about indicators that they might do well to look out for in an individual's attitudes to reminiscence and about possible methods of help and support. Above all they should avoid a 'this is the answer for all old people' approach. They should respect individual differences—delight in their existence—and take note of individuals' own views of their needs and destiny. Listening with genuine interest and empathy may often be the greatest service we can offer.

In drawing these introductory remarks to a close I would like to pay tribute to all the people who spoke with me and who are the subjects of this book. They have been so personally kind and generous to me. As a book about adjustment, a lot of stress falls inevitably on the difficulties these individuals faced. A number were depressed by the problems they confronted. But the overwhelming memory I am left with is of just how well they coped with life's trials and tribulations, with wisdom and good humour. There are sad stories in this book, but also stories of great resilience and courage, and of growth and development right through until late in life. These stories tell something of the riches that lie so often unnoticed behind our fellow citizens' front doors.

Chapter 2

Reminiscence, Ageing and Adjustment

The Study of Ageing and Adjustment

Of the various currents in gerontological thought within recent years, one of the most far reaching has been the development of a 'lifespan perspective' on ageing. Central to this perspective is an acknowledgement that to understand an individual's thoughts, feelings and behaviours in late life, one must also know something about his or her past experiences. With the acquisition of such a view in depth, it no longer seems sensible to equate one generation of older people with another. We see that different historical backgrounds produce quite different expectations of life and different norms of behaviour.

A lot of recent writing testifies to the importance to the study of ageing of historical knowledge (see, for example, Hareven and Adams, 1982). Previous ahistorical gerontological research now seems very naïve. For example the lower level of attainment shown by older people on intelligence tests carried out in the 1950s has largely been explained by differences in educational experience (Schaie, 1970). Even the lower activity and role performance levels of people of higher ages observed in the Kansas City study which gave rise to the 'disengagement' theory of ageing (Cumming and Henry, 1961), can be seen in retrospect to reflect generational characteristics as well as changes due to disability, retirement and other events particular to the individual. It has needed longitudinal study (in which the same individuals have been followed up over a long period of time) to overthrow some of the more simplistic ideas originally generated by age group comparisons, to show that neither an individual's intelligence nor his activity level necessarily declines with age.

Another, and equally as important, implication is that individuals will differ in their reactions to the experiences they encounter in old age according to their own personal life history. Such awareness has given birth to the term 'differential gerontology' (Thomae, 1976). We follow different paths, of disengagement or continued activity, for example, that are determined in part by the lifestyles we have already developed, which are themselves the product of opportunities derived from our sex, social class and education. The nature of this determination, it should be noted, is not always straightforward. For example we may not display artistic talents in old age because we have never learned to cultivate them earlier in life, but we may also choose to do certain things precisely because we were prevented earlier on. The effect is the reverse, but that there is a link with previous life experience is evident in both cases.

Sociology in comparison with psychology has a much stronger tradition of using biographical and autobiographical material to understand human development (see, for example, Rosenmayr, 1981). Its roots can be found in the European tradition of sociology which then spread to the United States, and are exemplified in the classic studies *The Polish Peasant in Europe and America* (Thomas and Znaniecki, 1918–20). Although the use of life story methods declined with the rise of 'objective' techniques as questionnaire and survey design, significant developments continued to take place. The concept of 'career' for example is now well established in sociological studies. It was used in a broader than occupational sense by Erving Goffman in his paper 'The moral career of the mental patient' more than 25 years ago (Goffman, 1959). Through the work of Becker (1963) and others the term was employed widely in deviancy studies. In his seminal paper 'That was your life: a biographical approach to later life', the British sociologist Malcolm Johnson was the first gerontologist to apply such concepts as 'biography' and 'career' to an understanding of ageing (Johnson 1976).

Despite the contributions of the psychoanalytic writers, psychology has been surprisingly backward in developing scientific studies based on people's own accounts of their lives. Only comparatively recently in work such as Daniel Levinson's *The Seasons of a Man's Life* (Levinson, 1978) have life history studies attained a measure of popularity within psychology. Lifespan psychology is, however, now developing strongly as a discipline, and a recent collection by Joep Munnichs and colleagues *Lifespan and Change in a Gerontological Perspective* (Munnichs *et al.* 1985) shows the importance of a biographical perspective to both the psychology and sociology of ageing and, moreover, the importance to studies of childhood and early adulthood of a gerontological perspective.

Nonetheless, despite the increasing interest in historical change and individual differences in ageing, normative models of human development still preserve their attraction. Although the current thinking on evolutionary development is that there is no 'biological' task for old age—that it is by definition survival beyond the time when the individual has any useful parenting function, and therefore has no natural principles to guide it—the 'existential' freedom thus offered the individual to choose his own goals for late life has not usually been found appealing by gerontologists. A search for theories, almost as a search for respectability, characterized social research on ageing through the 1950s and 1960s, marked in particular by the 'disengagement' versus 'activity' controversy on successful ageing. More recently there has been a reawakening of interest in the ideas of the psychoanalyst Carl Jung, whose special focus of interest was on the second half of life. His writings have for so long been overshadowed by the greater impact made by his contemporary and one-time colleague, Sigmund Freud. Yet Jung's writings comprise a remarkably rich grasp of the world's different cultures and are less tied to early twentieth century Europe.

His characterization of the second half of life as guided by different goals to the first, and being in essence 'religious'—involved in searching for and making contact with the sources of meaning in life, which Jung believed were expressed in symbolic terms within the individual's 'collective unconscious'—is a challenging and still under appreciated contribution to developmental psychology.

More well known to anyone who has studied human growth and development within a course of social work or other professional training, is Erik Erikson's theory of the stages of life, from the achievement of 'trust' in early childhood to 'integrity' in old age. The continuing attraction of the few pages that Erikson wrote on the characteristics of an ideal old age in his book *Childhood and Society* (Erikson, 1950), indicates something of the hunger for a meaningful view on the last part of life—and the lack of more substantial and comprehensible alternatives. Yet in the 30 years since his account was first written we have come to realize that the characteristics of 'integrity' that he describes—acceptance of one's past life without regrets, a harmonious view of past, present and future and a loss of fear of death—are rarely achieved (Clayton, 1975). This is no criticism of an ideal model, of course. But Erikson does seem to have been unaware of the extent to which human society can actively work against human development. Just as unemployment can threaten a sense of 'identity' and 'generativity', so can changed habits and values in society threaten the individual's own interpretation of his past life in old age or more likely threaten his adjustment to present society. Living to a great age in a fast changing society as the twentieth century requires many readaptations. Adjustment to old age is not only a matter of coming to terms with eventual physical decline and loss of friends and loved ones, it also involves coming to terms with discontinuities between the past and present and likely future.

Recent research in the study of late life adjustment has been considerable but unfortunately split between research of a clinical and psychiatric nature on the one hand and of a social and psychological nature on the other. We now have a better appreciation from epidemiological studies of the very high incidence of depressive illness in old age (Gurland and Toner, 1982) and the crucial role of physical and social loss in the onset of depression (Murphy, 1982). The treatment and prevention of depression among older people has become a challenging area for improving both medical and psychosocial intervention. Psychiatrists who are active in this field of work provide first hand knowledge of the difficult problems of adjustment that ageing raises, and how the losses incurred often highlight life-long issues of personality adjustment that have been absorbed by the various supports at work and at home which the individual has enjoyed up to then.

Yet these experiences of psychiatrists dealing with the hard end of human experience have too often been neglected by social researchers investigating the nature and determinants of constructs such as high morale and self esteem in late life. But as both are considering essentially the same phenomenon—human adjustment—a combined approach would be so much more fruitful (Coleman and McCulloch, 1985). The very extent of the problem of depression among older people means that it cannot be discounted as a pathological and exceptional condition. Depression is one of the 'normal' characteristics of old age, at least in Western society. In some of the most extensive and well carried out longitudinal studies on ageing, the Duke studies in the USA, the reported average percentage of depressed subjects at any one observation was 21.5 per cent, thus over one in five. The chances of any one individual becoming depressed at some time as they aged was much higher still. The implications of such a high incidence of late life depression for our understanding of the human life-span are profound. To quote the principal investigator, Ewald Busse:

'This longitudinal analysis of data demonstrates rather clearly that very few, even well-functioning elderly escape depression. The legacy of a long life appears to be a confrontation and struggle with the value of living. The issue for older people may well be not just survival but meaningful and purposeful existence' (Busse, 1985, p.220).

The Importance of Reminiscence

The manner in which reminiscence has come to feature in the study of ageing and adjustment is a remarkable one. It has changed its connotation from negative to positive—from being generally perceived as a symptom of mental deterioration to being valued as a normal if not essential component of success-ful ageing—all in the course of less than ten years.

It is important to remember just how negative views were. The situation is graphically described by Rose Dobrof, who was working in New York in the 1960s.

'I was then a very junior social worker on the staff of a home for the aged. I remember well being taught by our consulting psychiatrists and the senior social work staff about the tendency of our residents to talk about childhood in the shtetls of East Europe or arrival at Ellis Island or early years on the Lower East Side of New York. At best, this tendency was seen as an understandable, although not entirely healthy, preoccupation with happier times, understandable because these old and infirm people walked daily in the shadow of death. At worst, "living in the past" was viewed as pathology—regression to the dependency of the child, denial of the passage of time and the reality of the present, or evidence of organic impairment of the intellect. It was even said that "remembrance of things past" could cause or deepen depression among our residents, and God forgive us, we were to divert the old from their reminiscing through activities like bingo and arts and crafts' (Dobrof, 1984).

Even if sympathetic and seeking to be 'understanding', the attitude to reminiscence was demeaning. Many textbooks, for example, associated reminiscence with mental deterioration. The following example, from a textbook published in 1968 illustrates how the association was made, subtly but also with assurance.

'Elderly people, as is well known, spend an increasing amount of time talking and thinking about the past. It seems natural that as they feel out of the run of things, they should turn back to the days when life was more rewarding and enjoyable, and when events had a deeper impact on them. When the future holds little, and thinking about it arouses thoughts of death, interest will turn regressively to earlier years. Still, in most persons who become very old, the defect is more profound. The person becomes unable to recall recent events and lives more and more in the remote past, as if a shade were being pulled down over recent happenings, until nothing remains except memories of childhood. This type of memory failure depends on senile changes in the brain and is perhaps the most characteristic feature of senility. We do not properly understand why earlier memories are retained while more recent happenings are lost' (Lidz, 1968).

It is true that the formulators of 'disengagement theory' (Cumming and Henry, 1961) saw increased reminiscence as one manifestation of the process of ageing, which they understood as involving growing interiority and withdrawal from concerns with the outside world. Since their intent was to put forward disengagement as a normative process of adaptation to old age and death, reminiscence appeared in a more positive light. But the subsequent backlash against the thinking typified by disengagement theory—and in particular the research which demonstrated that the greater part of the withdrawal from involvement with the outside world shown by elderly individuals, was forced upon them rather than initiated by them—tended to confirm the original negative connotations given to reminiscence.

It is usually an oversimplification to attribute changes in attitudes within a field of study to a particular individual's contribution. Indeed it is often forgotten that the developmental psychologist Charlotte Bühler in Vienna had written, already in the 1930s, of reminiscence as an inevitable part of the ageing process resulting from the individual's need to substantiate his or her life in the face of loss of ability (Bühler, 1933). But a new interest in reminiscence was clearly awakened by a striking paper published in 1963 in the journal *Psychiatry* by the American psychiatrist Robert Butler, 'The life review: an interpretation of reminiscence in the aged' (Butler, 1963). I remember very well the excitement I felt when first reading this article a few years later. Quoting his own clinical experience as well as a wide range of literary authorities, Butler made out a case for viewing reminiscence as a normal activity in old age, the life review indeed as a process that people may have to undergo if they are to come to terms with their lives as they have lived them. Rose Dobrof, quoted above, testifies to the influence this single article had on attitudes to the elderly.

'In a profound sense, Butler's writings liberated both the old and the nurses, doctors and social workers; the old were free to remember, to regret, to look reflectively at the past and try to understand it. And we were free to listen, and to treat rememberers and remembrances with the respect they deserved, instead of trivializing them by diversion to a bingo game' (Dobrof, 1984).

Butler's article was followed by a number of other important contributions to the understanding of reminiscence. McMahon and Rhudick (1964) published a study of veterans of the Spanish-American war. They were struck by how well adjusted this particular group of men was, and also by the extent of reminiscing they displayed. Reminiscence therefore did not seem to be a negative sign, but on the contrary closely related to freedom from depression. They observed that the reminiscences of these men tended to be of a story-telling nature, meant to be entertaining and/or instructive, and McMahon and Rhudick related this to anthropological studies on the role of old people in primitive societies in preserving and handing on traditions. They also noted that the 'reminiscers' tended to exaggerate the value of the past in comparison with the present, claiming 'to have seen the best'. They suggested that reminiscence could play a significant role in the face of the losses of role and function in old age, in preserving self-respect by investing in the image of oneself as one had been, and stressing its importance.

Lewis took this idea further in an experimental study in which older people's expressed opinions were challenged in an authoritative fashion (Lewis, 1971). Those who were classified as 'reminiscers' on the basis of their conversation habits were shown to react differently to 'non-reminiscers'. Both groups had initially been asked to describe themselves as they used to be and as they were now. Whereas there was no difference at the outset between 'reminiscers' and 'non-reminiscers' in the degree of relationship they indicated between their past and present views of themselves, after being threatened in this way, the 'reminiscers' reacted by making their present self-concept much more consistent with their past self-concept. Lewis interpreted this identification with the past as a strategy, or 'defence', reminiscers used to deal with current threats to a sense of worthiness of self.

Butler, McMahon and Rhudick, and Lewis expressed some of the most influential ideas about reminiscence, and their articles are often cited by the more recent proponents of 'reminiscence therapy' in individual casework and group-work settings, in hospitals, residential homes and day care establishments. However, it also has to be acknowledged that a number of subsequent studies which followed up their work and tried to show in a rigorous way that reminiscence was related to individual adjustment, produced disappointing results.

Lieberman and Falk (1971) for example explored the function of reminiscence in three samples of older people: those who were living in their own homes; those who were waiting to enter old people's homes; and those who had been living in such institutions for some time. They found that those who were in the waiting situation were considerably more involved in reminiscence than either of the other two samples. But when they investigated whether degree of reminiscence was related to subsequent adaptation to the stress of moving, no relationship was found. Havighurst and Glasser (1972) did identify an associated pattern between high personal-social adjustment, positive effect of reminiscence and high frequency of reminiscence, but their study was not able to clarify the direction of causation. Taken altogether, as many studies seem to have found no evidence for the adaptive value of reminiscence as have found positive evidence (see Merriam, 1980; Merriam and Cross, 1982).

Reminiscence therapy therefore cannot be said to stand on a very solid base, and recent commentators, notably Merriam (1980) have been led to criticize simplistic thinking about reminiscing and its value. Talking or thinking about the past may serve various functions, and we must try to be more discerning in our observations. Reminiscence, too, may mean different things to individuals in different situations. For example a frail disabled elderly person may learn to appreciate thinking back on past memories in a way yet inconceivable to a younger, active person. Moreover, as already mentioned at the beginning of this chapter, we have to be prepared to accept that there may not be any general laws of social or psychological ageing to be found. Whether a person stands to gain from reminiscence will depend on his past history as well as his present needs. More detailed analysis of individual cases therefore seems to be called for, using diverse samples of older people.

Functions of Reminiscence

It is important to note that already in the first writings on reminiscence, quite a divergence of views was expressed on the function reminiscence might play in old age. Butler suggested that the life review was a normative process in later life, prompted by the realization of approaching death. It was 'characterized by the progressive return to consciousness of past experience, and, particularly, the resurgence of unresolved conflicts' (Butler, 1963). He stressed, as have later writers (for example, Kaminsky, 1984), that the life review is not necessarily easy to recognize. It can appear fragmentary with key themes occurring in dream material as well as in conscious daydreaming and more purposeful thinking. Typically ordinary daily occurrences may trigger thinking on associated events in the past.

Ingmar Bergman's film *Wild Strawberries* is cited both by Butler (1963) and Erikson (1978) as an example of the process of life reviewing. This is the story of an egocentric professor who becomes aware of his failings by a process of dreams and of conscious recollection of family relationships and his place within them, and as a result is led to seek reconciliation with his estranged son and daughter-in-law. However, Butler is careful to stress that the outcome of the life review is not necessarily positive. The individual may remain obsessed with events and actions he regrets, find no solution and no peace, and develop chronic feelings of guilt and depression. It is also possible that the individual may 'block' the life review process altogether, succeed in avoiding certain thoughts and reject the past. This might be a successful way of avoiding a negative outcome, particularly if the individual has plenty of present interests, but it denies the potentiality of growth inherent in the life review process.

Close similarities can be seen between the concept of a normative life review and Erik Erikson's earlier notion of the achievement of integrity as the final task of life. Indeed Butler's theory may be regarded as an extension of one of the key notions in Erikson's last stage, as it suggests a process whereby 'acceptance of one's one and only life cycle' is or is not achieved.

McMahon's and Rhudick's observations on how much time the veterans they interviewed devoted to talking about the past led them to speculate on a number of other uses of reminiscence: '...the maintenance of self-esteem in the face of declining physical and intellectual abilities; coping with grief and depression resulting from personal losses; finding means to contribute significantly to a society of which older persons are members; and retaining some sense of identity in an increasingly estranged environment' (McMahon and Rhudick, 1964). They also explicitly linked their ideas to the life cycle theories of Erikson, by saying that the adaptational significance of reminiscence can best be understood in the light of Erikson's view that identity formation is a lifelong task.

The close link between reminiscence and preservation of identity is stressed by a number of other psychotherapists: see Castelnuovo-Tedesco (1978), Zinberg and Kaufman (1963). The same idea is expressed by social workers arguing for the value of groupwork using reminiscence with older people: '. . .reaching out to share recollections with others may be motivated by the need to convince oneself of a continuity between the past and present' (Carlson, 1984). A similar point is made by the author Ronald Blythe. 'One of the reasons why old people make so many journeys into the past is to satisfy themselves that it is still there' (Blythe, 1979). The past represents a platform of security which may give strength and effort to continue.

However, maintaining a sense of identity is quite a distinct idea from the life review. Indeed McMahon and Rhudick dispute the implication of Butler's view that all individuals feel a need for self justification at the end of their lives, and indeed rather denigrate this function as characteristic of 'obsessive-compulsive subjects who, we may suspect, have been reviewing their past behaviour in the same judgemental and evaluative way all their lives', i.e. it is evidence of a lifelong and on-going pathological process.

For McMahon and Rhudick, if there is an ideal use of reminiscence it is the one traditionally ascribed to older men in primitive societies, as bearers and transmitters of their culture's stories and traditions. They describe their 'best-adjusted' group, quite simply, as storytellers, 'recounting past exploits and experiences with obvious pleasure in a manner which is both entertaining and informative'. Moreover, these storytellers seemed to have little need to depreciate the present or glorify the past, as did other members of their sample. Rather their reminiscing is a happy instance of behaviour serving both personal ends and social goals. 'The older person's knowledge of a bygone era provides him with an opportunity to enhance his self-esteem by contributing in a meaningful way to his society.'

It has to be admitted that the storytelling function of the old has become devalued in modern societies, both because of the fast changing nature of society which has appeared to make the past seem less relevant, and because of the development of many other means of preserving and communicating information. Nevertheless, the recent growth of interest in oral history has done something to reverse this trend. It has led to a revaluing of the memories ordinary individuals possess of the times they have lived through. The memories of the oldest generations have come to appear especially valuable, with the realization that the possibility of collecting records of experiences of a whole era, such as the Edwardian period before the First World War, dies with them.

In their recent book *The Experience of Old Age, Stress, Coping and Survival*, which presents a detailed psychological investigation of elderly people moving into homes for the aged based of many years' research and reflection, Lieberman and Tobin clearly express their support for an identity maintenance or defence rather than a developmental view of the function of reminiscence. The particular data on which their perspective on reminiscence is based were taken from a longitudinal study of 85 elderly people awaiting admission to homes in the Chicago area. They demonstrated the existence of much reworking of the past among the people they interviewed, but believed that it was rarely equatable with the process of life reviewing as described by Butler.

'Like the life review, it involves considerable effort and reorganization, but rather than reconciliation with one's personal past, such reorganization is the creation of an image. It serves, we believe, to resolve a critical dilemma posed by the issues of old age and leads not to serenity but rather to stability' (Lieberman and Tobin, 1983, p. 309).

Reminiscence they argue often serves the purpose of creating a 'myth', a story that justifies their lives and is intended to be believed. Typically the elderly person portrays him or herself as the central figure or hero in a drama that is worth telling or worth having lived for. They criticize the concept of the life review for its implicit assumption 'that humans function only at the highest level', whereas most people do not have the high level of inner skills to undertake a sorting and restructuring of the past. They do not thereby intend to belittle reminiscence. Indeed the main burden of their book is to demonstrate that an essential task of old age is the preservation of a coherent, consistent self in the face of loss and of threat of loss. Reminiscence has a valuable role to play in this defence.

The views of Lieberman and Tobin on the importance of 'myth' in the psychology of old age, and related observations in the work of Langer on the contribution of subjective perception of control to adjustment in institutionalized people (Langer, 1983), and of Sherman on the value of a phenomenological perspective to counselling older persons (Sherman, 1981, 1984) are comparatively new perspectives in psychology. Still it was already clear at the time when my own research on reminiscence began in 1969, that it was possible to see the function of reminiscence in older people in a variety of ways. I therefore took care from the outset to record carefully the reminiscence I observed, and to seek to categorize its character, whether 'analytic' or 'informative', 'self' or 'society' focussed, and to relate it to the individual's life circumstances.

The account of the study that follows takes note of the various views that have been expressed about the functions of reminiscence: the life review, the story-telling role, the creation of a meaningful myth and the maintenance of self esteem. It pays attention to the very real problems of adjustment that face older people, and describes depression where it is present as well as successful coping. It takes account of both a lifespan and life situation perspective to understanding the psychology of old age. Above all it tries to focus on the person and to present analyses and judgements at the level of the individual case, drawing conclusions from the evidence available as to how reminiscence is or is not contributing to that particular individual's life.

Chapter 3

Living Alone in Sheltered Housing in London circa 1970

The Nature of the Study

The sample

This study is of the lives, attitudes, and in particular, the attitudes to reminiscence, of older people living alone in sheltered housing schemes in the London area. It is important to emphasize this point since we have learned from earlier research not only how individuals' behaviour may be shaped by the physical and social circumstances of their lives, but also how living circumstances may say something about their personalities. Caution is required in attempting to draw wider generalizations on the basis of a study on individuals from one particular background. Yet selection is necessary in social research. We can only maintain coherence by focussing in turn on different groups within society. The investigator, however, must take care to specify the distinguishing characteristics of the people he has chosen to be the subjects of his research.

The work reported in this book was begun in 1969 when I was a postgraduate research student in psychology, based at Bedford College in the University of London. I was then aged 22. I had chosen ageing as the area of study in which to do research, and had identified reminiscence as an interesting topic for enquiry. In particular, I had been impressed by the recent writings of Butler and of McMahon and Rhudick that were discussed in the previous chapter. In the years that I was registered for the degree of PhD at the university (1969–72) I interviewed many older people. Because of the nature of the research methodology I opted for, which involved a number of visits to each individual, I developed a close relationship with many of the people I visited, and I continued to visit them after my course of study had finished and after I had left London. I recognized the potential scientific value of continuing to record the details about each individual's life and the attitudes he or she expressed. This book is thus the product of more than 15 years' acquaintance with some of the people concerned—only a very small number, of course, are still alive today.

The people I visited were all initially living in sheltered housing schemes, that is, in one- or two-roomed apartments within housing blocks provided by the district housing departments and specifically intended for older people. The term 'sheltered housing' is usually restricted to housing schemes where a variously termed 'warden' or 'housemother' or 'caretaker' also lives on the premises. Such a person is responsible to the housing department for supervizing the upkeep of the fabric, but also usually has a 'good neighbour' function in keeping an eye on the well-being of the tenants themselves and calling in help from health or social services when necessary. Sheltered housing is now also provided by commercially based housing companies and by housing associations. It is also possible in certain instances to buy a sheltered housing apartment on a long-term lease. However, with the exception of one housing association scheme, all the schemes I visited were run by district councils, and all the apartments were rented by the people living in them.

I visited schemes in five London boroughs, three north of the River Thames, in Westminster, Camden and Brent, all in easy travelling distance from where I had lodgings, and two south of the river in Merton and Kingston, near to my parents' home. Together, they contained residents from a wide range of social and economic circumstances. Altogether I visited 16 sites of varying sizes from 15 to 50 apartments and approached a small number of people living within each scheme. I thought it best to avoid interviewing too many within any one building. I considered that problems might arise from individuals sensing a threat to their privacy in my talking to their neighbours as well. It is commonly observed that it is often easier to speak openly to someone who is clearly identified as a stranger and has no connection with others who know one. Moreover, people living in such close proximity as sheltered housing schemes do naturally tend to speak about one another. I wanted to minimize any concern that might be felt about the confidentiality of some information given to me. At the same time I wanted to avoid stimulating too much curiousity about what other tenants had said to me. A further advantage of selecting from a larger number of sheltered housing schemes is the greater credibility it gives to generalizing the findings from this study to people living within sheltered housing schemes in London at this period of time.

I chose sheltered housing as a starting point for my research partly because of its convenience as designated housing for older people and because I could ask for assistance from the wardens both in making my selection of people to visit and in gaining introductions. I also considered that sheltered housing inhabitants were likely to be physically frailer than an ordinary sample of older people living in their own homes, and that other 'losses' too were likely to have led them to come to sheltered housing in the first place—bereavement of spouse in particular. 'Loss' of their old familiar living environment and separation from friends and neighbours were also likely to be more evident in older people living in sheltered housing than in the general population. Since the function that reminiscence might have in helping an individual cope with the losses of ageing was uppermost in my mind, it made sense to identify a population of older people where loss was clearly evident. At the same time, institutions as residential care homes or hospitals appeared to be less easy environments in which to carry out this type of research, mainly because of the difficulties in having a truly private conversation—certainly in the late 1960s and early 1970s when very few people, even in residential care homes, had their own rooms.

Also for reasons of developing a close one-to-one relationship, I chose only to interview people living alone, therefore those who were widowed or single or divorced/separated. The only other conditions I asked the wardens to consider when identifying names of people for me to visit were that they should not be living in close proximity, for reasons already stated, (I stressed in fact that I wanted to see a representative section of older people) and that they should be at least have attained the age of 70. In the event, the age range of the people I visited extended from 68 to 92 years, which is of course a very wide age variation. In the two years in which I built up my sample, I visited a total of 76 people, 43 women and 33 men. Of these I have excluded 26 from the main analyses reported in this book, mainly because I did not obtain sufficient data, either measures of conversation or psychometric data, to allow me to feel justified in making comparable judgements about their attitudes. Eight of the sample died before sufficient data were collected, 16 were either unwilling to co-operate in such research or unable, at least at the times I visited them, to provide me with all the information I needed on which to base my judgements. The data I obtained on two other people I later had to exclude from the analysis—from one because he proved eventually to have a wife who did sometimes share the household with him, and the other because he did not actually live in 'sheltered housing', as the block he lived in had no resident warden. But for illustrative purposes, I have included the latter's case study in Chapter 9.

The group of people whose characteristics I wish to describe in this and the following chapter, therefore, comprise 27 women and 23 men, with an average age of 80 years. As will be expected from a random sample of older people, the women had a higher average age, 15 being of 80 years and over compared with only eight of the men. The balance in marital status, however, was very similar between the two sexes. The majority in both groups were widowed. Six of the women and four of the men were single. One of the men was divorced. The group came from a mixed working class and middle class background, with a quite considerable variation in previous occupational status.

The data collected

My approach to each person in the first instance was as a friendly visitor, a university student interested both in the processes of ageing and in the welfare services available for older people. In the first meetings I encouraged people to speak about matters that interested or concerned them, and the variety of attitudes expressed towards reminiscence struck me quite early on. Some spoke a lot about the course of their past lives, others told stories based on past experience, whereas others still were more concerned to talk about their own present day situation or more generally about the state of the world. From the outset, I recorded the main themes and features of their conversation, noting down the chief lines it had taken shortly after I completed my visit.

Relatively little scientific consideration has been given by psychologists to ways of recording and analysing the content of natural free flowing conversation, as opposed to non-lexical and expressive dimensions of verbal behaviour (e.g. hesitances, silences, pitch, etc). Most have relied on clinical interpretative judgements on the 'meaning' of what is being said (see, for example, Gottschalk *et al.*, 1961, 1963). One important exception, however, is the work of Eugene Gendlin on assessing the individual's capacity to introspect on feelings, evident from the client's conversation in Rogerian therapy, for example (Gendlin, 1962, 1981), which is very relevant to an analysis of certain functions associated with reminiscence, as the 'life review' (see Sherman, 1984). Also of interest are the attempts to rate the general functional characteristics of spontaneous speech following Morris's and Austin's classifications of language in terms of modes and uses ('referring to', 'evaluating', 'seeking to inform of', 'prescribing', etc) (Austin, 1962; Morris, 1946, see, for example Soskin and John, 1963). Such methods of course also depend on more than overt criteria as individual words, but do not go beyond natural 'common-sense' judgements about what an individual 'means' by what he says, and are easy to validate.

In my initial conversations with the people I met, I continued to promote open-ended conversations, encouraging them to speak about matters that interested them. The notes I took afterwards gave me a sense of useful categories I could apply in describing the general characteristics of each person's conversation with me. Eventually I refined the system into a relatively simple and applicable one. After each conversation I recorded as best I could the content of each person's conversation in terms of four general dimensions:

— whether the information spoken had been about the individual or about other family members or particular others;
— whether the information pertained to the past (defined pragmatically as referring to events occurring at least five years previously) or to the present and future;
— whether information and/or opinions were expressed about general affairs of the world in the past or present; and
— whether the individual had provided psychological information, analysis or evaluation about his or her actions, thoughts and feelings.

Using such categories I was able to structure my account of the individual's conversation and also to give a crude rating of the predominance of different features in the conversation. I continued to use the same broad categories for describing conversation in subsequent visits.

Once I felt I had got to know each person I asked permission to tape record a conversation and had these records (of an hour's length) transcribed. This allowed me to rate the same categories more rigorously and to develop measures of conversation content (e.g. of amount of reminiscence, family, world affairs, psychological ... conversation), in addition validating the cruder assessments from memory as well as validating the categories themselves by obtaining independent assessments of the content of conversation. These methods have been described in detail elsewhere (Coleman, 1972, 1974). I tape recorded two conversations from most of the people in the study and in some instances tape recorded a further session ten years later.

In the tape recorded sessions some structure was given to the conversation by the introduction of standardized cues based primarily on the 'past' dimension (see Chapter 4 for further details). In practice I found that in many cases I often needed to say very little in the tape recorded session except to give supportive encouragement to the things that the individuals wanted to talk about. If they did not appear interest in following up the reminiscing cues they were not pressed further and the conversation was supported by cues about the present.

Besides rating these various features of their conversations, I also began early on to note down my own impressionistic reactions to the situation I met and the things that were said, which I have found very useful in subsequently formulating case study accounts on individuals. This information also provides useful corrective information on my own biases and focus of interest. As I got to know people better, I also invited them to help me in my research by answering questions from set questionnaires. Over a period of two years I administered the following six questionnaires:

1. *An Assessment of Life Change* in particular role areas, which was a form I constructed on the basis of earlier work (especially Townsend, 1957; Tunstall, 1966) to collect information on changes in social contact and activities since the age of 60 in defined areas of life: namely sharing a household, in relation to work or any other organization, with children and other relatives, and with friends and neighbours.
2. A short *Functioning Health Rating Scale* (Rosow and Breslau, 1966) designed to provide a simple uni-dimensional rating of functional health.
3. The 20 item *Life Satisfaction Index (LSIA)* developed at the University of Chicago by Neugarten *et al.* (1961) and asking about satisfaction with both present and past life.
4. The 30 item *Depression Scale* from the *Minnesota Multiphasic Personality Inventory Scale* derived by Dempsey (1964) to give a uni-dimensional rating of depression.
5. A detailed *Questionnaire on Reminiscence* of 48 items, developed in America by Havighurst and Glasser (1972) to explore attitudes to reminiscence.
6. The *Cattell 16 Personality Factor Inventory*, a long questionnaire with 90 items designed to provide a profile on 16 separate aspects of personality (Cattell and Eber, 1966). (In the event, I only asked a small number of people to fill this in for me. I shall therefore only refer to results obtained from its use in certain of the case studies described in Chapters 5 to 9).

I repeated the first five questionnaires with the survivors in 1980–81 (i.e. ten years after the original data collection).

The focus of the research study from the outset was on reminiscence, and in the following chapter a detailed presentation will be made of the data I analysed on attitudes to reminiscence and to past life generally, derived both from the questionnaire and from the individual's conversation (both tape and hand recorded). But to set these attitudes in context, I shall comment in the remainder of this chapter on the characterizing features of this sample of people: their past and present lives, their present state of morale, their attitudes to sheltered housing and to contemporary society, concluding with a few brief observations about their subsequent longevity.

Past History

Since at the time that I interviewed them in 1970–71, the youngest person in the sample was 68 and the oldest 92 years, virtually all had been born in the reign of Queen Victoria. A number remembered being taken as a child to see the old Queen pass in the street. Some of them remembered particular historical events associated with their birth and childhood. The oldest man described how he had been called the 'Michaelmas Goose'. He had been born in 1878, the year he said that it had snowed in September!

The type of life history of people born in this period is well summarized by Mark Abrams in the introduction to his survey study of older people, *Beyond Three-Score and Ten* (Abrams, 1978). Most of the people had been born in the London area and the circumstances of London life in the 1880s and 1890s were described in detail in the work of Charles Booth, *Life and Labour of the People in London* published between 1889 and 1897. Booth's survey showed that one-third of all London families lacked sufficient income to afford a diet that would keep them above the starvation level. The principal causes of this widespread absolute poverty Booth concluded were not to be found in: '...crime, vice, drinks or laziness, (but in the) lack of work, death of husband, sickness, trade misfortune, old age, and accident'. Signs of this poverty were evident in the lives of many of the people in my study. A number described the hard times consequent on accident to or death of the breadwinner in their family, and the struggle of many families to keep together. Seven of the women (Miss Smith for example whose case study is presented in Chapter 5) had gone into service with another family when young, mainly as a result of poverty in their own families following the death of a parent. All of them, it was noteworthy, spoke in positive terms of their experience of service.

A slightly older group than Abrams' sample, almost all the men had qualified for military service in the First World War. Nearly all had had their lives disturbed by the war. For many men, it was the single theme which dominated their reminiscences as they recounted the historical events, the particular horrors they had witnessed, the comradeship and the humour too. A number described themselves as being 'marked for life' by experiences they could not forget. Many women in the sample had suffered personal loss, too, because of the war. Nearly all had lost brothers or other close relatives. Two had lost husbands and one her 'sweetheart' (she had never married). The husbands of a further two women had been badly handicapped with grave consequences for the family. Both wives had had to go out to work whilst still bringing up their families. Most women had borne their children in the period following the First World War when birthrates became much lower than in the preceding Victorian and Edwardian periods. The average number of children born to the married people in the sample was only just two per person, while 17 per cent had had no children, and 60 per cent had had only one or two children.

The economic slump of the early 1930s had also had a large influence. Many of the men described periods of looking for new work and periods of being without work. Two men described how the small businesses they had set up were ruined in this period. For three of the men in the sample, difficulties in work were the main reason they had not been able to marry. In the Second World War, there were further tragedies. One man had lost both his sons at sea, another woman her husband, and another man his first wife in a bomb blast. Three other people had their houses destroyed by bombing and their lives disturbed.

In retrospect, however, it should be said how remarkably well these people seem to have coped with such difficulties in their lives. Furthermore, a number of people had developed high self-esteem from the same events. One man's life had been 'transformed' by his career in the army. Another man's tug had helped in the relief operations at Dunkirk. The First World War for another had meant a number of interesting years of travel in India, which he greatly enjoyed. A number of women, and four in particular, had enjoyed their periods of work during the Second World War.

Loss and Adjustment

A major characterizing feature of the latter years of life is the relatively greater number of severity of losses individuals are faced with, both physically and socially. This fact is accentuated in modern Western society in part because of the high proportion of the population who now live to grow old, but principally because loss has become a less frequent occurrence earlier in life. Individuals are less likely to be confronted by life threatening disease and disabling conditions when young. In turn they are largely shielded from the impact of death among those around them. Not many generations back, the death of one's siblings in early life brought a close acquaintance with death at a young age. Funerals in the family were a common occurrence. Yet nowadays many people reach mid-life without having experienced the death of a close relative other than grandparents. Death has come to be concentrated in old age, and experiencing the deaths of friends and relatives in close succession is something an older person must learn to live with.

At the time when I first met them, there was a considerable degree of variation in the amount of physical and social loss individuals had incurred in recent years. A number of the people had confronted considerable loss. Many had suffered an important bereavement. A number, too, had suffered a striking change in their vigour and abilities. Considering just the loss of spouse, of the 39 widows in the sample, 15 had been widowed in the previous six years (nine of the men and six of the women) but a number had been widowed many years previously

—two women were war widows of the First World War, more than 50 years previously. As regards the ability to provide for themselves, to go out shopping, to do their cooking and housework, nearly two-thirds, 31 people, were fully independent in this sense (16 of the men and 15 of the women). When I first met them, 15 received help either with their housework or with the preparation of meals (five of the men and ten of the women). Eight were completely housebound (four of the men and four of the women).

A degree of resilience is needed to cope with the buffets of old age. Many not surprisingly found it difficult to keep going. The high incidence of depression in late life has now been recorded by a number of authorities (Gurland and Toner, 1982) but is still inadequately recognized by the helping professions. Feelings of depression and low morale as measured by the Life Satisfaction Index and the MMPI Depression Scale corresponded closely to both physical and social loss. The highest correlations obtained (averaging over 0.6) were with measures of relative social loss in the last five years or since the age of 60, i.e. taking into account social role areas in which an individual had been active and expressing lost roles as a proportion of this.

A number of the people I visited were depressed. Taking into account their answers on the two morale questionnaires, and other things they said to me, I rated 18 people (ten men and eight women) i.e. over one-third of my sample, as being significantly demoralized. These were people who on both the Life Satis-faction and Depression Scales admitted to frequent feelings of depression and who indicated as well a number of other signs of disturbed mood (loss of interest, loss of self-esteem, loss of initiative, tenseness, lack of concentration, feelings of weakness and illness and sleep disturbance).

The high association between loss and morale is also evident from the fact that of the ten 'demoralized' men, six had lost their wives in the last six years (compared with three of the 30 men who were not demoralized). Another two were housebound. The eight 'demoralized' women were not as obviously subjects of severe loss. One had lost her husband in the last six years, two were housebound and a further two needed help in the household. Nevertheless, the over-all relationship between loss and demoralization was clear also for the women, even when defining loss in crude objective terms without taking into account its meaning for the individual.

On the other hand, it would be wrong to overstress the negative features for this group of older people. A number were very happy people. A rating of very high level of morale was given to those who indicated that by and large life was as interesting and enjoyable for them in old age as it had been in younger years, as evidenced by responses both on the life satisfaction and depression question-naires. Twelve people expressed such attitudes, five men and seven women. All were coping well with life. Yet they too had difficulties to contend with. One man was virtually blind, but maintained his independence remarkably well. He even managed to keep up his yearly holiday visits to friends in Austria. Two of the women were severely limited, one by rheumatoid arthritis and the other by angina, which kept her housebound, but both maintained close links with their families and were highly valued by the people around them. But there were also other individuals without families, who succeeded in finding a lot of interest in life and thereby maintained a very high level of morale.

This then was the background against which I attempted to assess how significant a role reminiscence might play in the individual's life. Did it offer some protection against the impact of loss? Did it provide a rationale for living in later life after major roles were relinquished? Even if it did not provide a major source of support, what was the nature of the enjoyment reminiscence provided? Or was it on the other hand a 'necessary' activity, as Butler has suggested in his concept of the life review? If so, why did some people not appear to reminisce? Interviewing a group of individuals of whom a large number were struggling with recent or with impending loss, seemed a fruitful context in which to explore the functions of reminiscence. But before turning to their attitudes to reminiscence, it is important to describe also their attitudes to the housing and to the society in which they lived.

Attitudes to Sheltered Housing

For a long time, and certainly in the period in which I carried out my initial study, the provision of sheltered housing by local authorities was thought of as an unqualified good, a positive feature of British social policy for older people which offset the shabby history of residential care provision. Some of the fiercest critics of residential care homes in the UK, as Peter Townsend in his classic exposé of conditions inherited from the workhouse in his book *The Last Refuge* (1962) even went so far as to argue that such institutions could be abolished and replaced by an increased sheltered housing provision, together with improved domiciliary services. A considerable amount of sheltered housing was provided in the 1960s and 1970s and it is only recently that questions have been raised about the benefits of providing more of this type of special accommodation (Butler *et al.*, 1983). It may not always be the most beneficial action for a person to move away from their old environment. Helping people to stay in their own homes may often make more sense, by making alterations to the fittings and establishing community support services (Wheeler, 1982; Tinker, 1984). Furthermore, the claim that people will feel less isolated living in a sheltered housing complex is often not borne out. Communal rooms are often not used, and an individual can be as lonely behind his front door in a block of flats as in an ordinary house.

It does not therefore seem so surprising now that many people in the study complained about living in a sheltered housing complex. These were predominantly —but not exclusively—persons who also expressed low feelings of morale in general. Still it is noteworthy that for 16 people (five of the men and eleven of the women), almost one-third of the sample, significant features of their conversation were negative comments about the sheltered housing scheme they lived in. Either they had regrets about leaving their old environment, or else they had specific complaints about, for instance, the distance from shops, and other general facilities, or the lack of friendliness within the scheme. Often they said all these things. Many, therefore, did not feel at home living in sheltered housing. A number commented on how their lives had been disrupted by the move.

'...Sometimes when I am sitting here on my own, I think to myself, "Oh, I wish I was down in my old house, I would have somebody to talk to," ... if I went and stood at the front gate and any of them saw you, they'd wave to you, you don't get nothing of that here...'

'...I wish I had never left Wembley. She said I was coming to Brondesbury Park and it sounded all right, but she didn't say it was near Willesden and Harlesden ... if I'd known I wouldn't have come...'

'...I was always used to seeing a lot of people and then you come to this...'

'...The monotony of being boxed up here, it drives you barmy, there's heaps of places I would like to go to. We've got that confounded walk every time to get to the bus, then you've got to walk all the way back uphill...'

'...When I applied for it, I said, "Am I near the shops?" They said, "Yes." I nearly had a fit when I saw the shops, because where I was I only had to go across the road...'

There were also those who were appreciative of the benefits of sheltered housing. Four people in particular had positive comments to make. One lady explained how moving had helped her to have more contact than she used to.

'...I have more contact now ... I see a great many people. You see when you live in a basement you really are right away from everything.'

However, it must be said that negative comments outweighed the positive ones.

Attitudes to Society

Another dislocation older people face which has only begun to be given much attention is the global change in the nature of the society in which they live. Although a common perspective on ageing is on change experienced by the person, in many ways older people display great continuity between their past and present in their basic activities, interests and values. Stability of attitudes is the finding of most longitudinal studies that have followed people in later life over a number of years. Indeed it is often the outer world that has changed most. An expert on human cognitive functioning, Patrick Rabbitt, has compared older people recently to time travellers (Rabbitt, 1984).

'...People now aged 80 are time travellers, exiled to a foreign country which they now share with current 20 year olds. These groups have been fed, housed and educated very differently, have received, or failed to receive, different medical treatment for different conditions, have been taught to prize different skills and attitudes, and have been shaped by dramatically different experiences.'

It is worth reflecting on just how many social changes this group of people had witnessed in their lifetimes. One man, for example, remembered how he had seen a motor car for the first time.

'...We were living just the other side of Lewisham. It was more like a village in those days of course. I recollect my old dad, he was in the front and I was in the back garden. He said, "Come quickly". Like a boy I rushed out to see what it was. It was the first motor car he had seen and I had seen and there was a man walking in front of it with a red flag. It was 1896...'

But it is the value change within society in an individual's life time which can be the most disturbing in the latter part of life. Jeremy Seabrook has identified such problems from his own interviews with older people (Seabrook, 1980).

'...Many of the old grew up in the world where they had to be disciplined, frugal, stoical, self-denying, poor; and what this taught them, often in bitterness and pain, appears to be of no use to their children and grandchildren, who have been shaped for different purposes by changed circumstances...'

In a recent and yet unpublished study in Southampton on older people's attitudes, Andrew McCulloch (1985) has adopted the concept of 'moral siege' to describe a set of attitudes characteristic of a large number of the people he interviewed also living in sheltered housing accommodation. Such people actively compared the past with the present, emphasizing differences between the generations rather than similarities, and giving a high moral estimation to old people and a low one to the young. Strongly associated too was a tendency to attribute changes in society to the upheavals of the First and Second World Wars. McCulloch argues that many people feel obliged to condemn modern society because this continuity is too great to bridge. Accepting the values of modern society is tantamount to denying meaning to their own lives as they have led them. McCulloch is careful to point out that to properly understand people who feel this way, one must be prepared to consider whether they are right, a point echoed by Seabrook.

'...The old ... have lived through loss of function, destruction of role, forfeit of purpose and often of meaning. The old demonstrate to us ... the price we have paid for what we are pleased to see as our material progress...'

Such work as that by Seabrook and McCulloch helps make much more understandable what is often seen as a fault of older people. The veteran journalist, Mary Stott, in her book *Ageing for Beginners*, which attempts to dispel negative stereotypes of ageing, quotes her younger colleague, Jill Tweedie, writing in *The Guardian*.

'...Whenever I pass a group of old men or old women, I can hear the keening note in their voices as they list for each other the iniquities of today ... the elderly are remarkably conformist, no matter how unique each of them might have been in their youth, which is why younger people have difficulty in regarding them as individuals. Old age has a vested interest in decline, a profit motive in refusing to acknowledge improvement...' (quoted by Stott, 1981 p. 3)

Mary Stott's reaction is to reject such images as unreal, as projections on the part of younger people of what they fear to become. But I suspect that the failure to understand is of a different nature. It is not that older people do not criticize the young. It is that we are insensitive to the very understandable reasons why they do so criticize. It is harder to die in a society that is changing, in a society that is different from the one that one was brought up in, a point brought out by George Orwell in a passage written nearly 50 years ago.

'...It's also true that people then had something that we haven't got now. What? It was simply that they didn't think of the future as something to be terrified of. It isn't that life was softer then than now. Actually, it was harsher ... and yet what was it that people had in those days? A feeling of security, even when they weren't secure. More exactly, it was a feeling of continuity. All of them knew they'd got to die ... but what they didn't know was that the order of things could change ... it's easy enough to die if the things you care about are going to survive ... individually they were finished but their way of life would continue ...' (Orwell, 1939)

The attitude of 'moral siege,' therefore, is a way of coping with social change which enables individuals to remain satisfied with their own past lives. It is not entirely satisfactory, however, because the old person will always experience some social pressure to adopt more modern values. There are others indeed who are confused by change and are left in a no man's land between their own past values and beliefs and the values of a new world, an unhappy state which Andrew McCulloch calls 'questioning'. In McCulloch's study 'questioning' was represented by an association between the failure to understand modern society and a questioning of personal religious beliefs, in particular, belief in a beneficient God. Also associated was a low level of thought about the past, which would suggest that such people found difficulty in finding solace in reminiscing. Still others managed to transcend the differences between past and present, and achieved a sense of continuity or even of progress with which they could identify their own lives. But such a state of harmony with a changing world does not appear easy to achieve.

Certainly many of the people I interviewed, who it should be noted were similar to McCulloch's study group in that both groups lived in sheltered housing, expressed dissatisfaction with contemporary society. I asked each person to compare past and present life, and indeed for many this was a noticeable theme in their conversation. Out of the 50 questioned, 32 expressed a substantially negative view on the present and only nine people judged present society over all to be as 'good' as the society they had been brought up in.

The most common critical theme was of the amount of dissatisfaction expressed in contemporary society. At least 15 people raised this in explicit terms Even some of those who were concerned to stress that living conditions were much better today, qualified this judgement by pointing to people's declining satisfaction with their conditions. It was a case of 'much wants more' said one man. People were not as happy.

'...Thank God things are better, but I'm just wondering whether people are any happier ... walk down the road and see what should be smiling faces, happier and better off, God Almighty, you never hear a blasted person sing or look happy...'

'...I like the old days far far better. Everybody seemed happier and jollier, even though the money in those days was very, very little, but we all got through...'

The decline in satisfaction was often attributed to an increasing selfishness in individuals' lives.

'...Everyone seems to be eaten up with better conditions, and they are better conditions, but it hasn't made them any happier, it seems to have made them more selfish than anything else...'

'...Everybody seems to think more of themselves than anybody else, as long as they are all right well that's OK, doesn't matter about anybody else, self first, self last, anything left self again...'

Of particular aspects of society that worried them, the most commonly mentioned was the behaviour of children and young people. At least one-third of the sample brought this up spontaneously in their conversation. Most attributed the responsibility for lowering standards of behaviour to declining surveillance by parents. Home life had been better in the past. Families cared more about what happened to their children. For a number a greater harshness had spread into life as a whole. Many too deplored the attitudes to work of working men, and there was a lot of criticism of strikes and trade unions.

A number appeared genuinely disturbed by the changes in society around. The expression 'can't understand things anymore' often came up in conversation. The speed of change worried some people. Some said it was not the same country.

'...It is not England any more, it's a muck heap...'

In this context of generally critical comments on present society, the positive views stood out. The most commonly referred to positive change was the improvement in welfare services—twelve people referred directly to it. A number were keen to dispel the myth of the 'good old days'. There has been little help for the poor unemployed in the past. The provision of social security payments had been a good thing. The workhouse had been a fearful institution and the destination for many people as they grew old after a lifetime's work. If one wanted to know what conditions last century had been like, Charles Dickens' writings gave a good guide, said one man. Even so, those who spoke sympathetically of changed times, and changed behaviour, for example on the part of the young, were very few.

There was no noticeable link between positive and negative attitudes to contemporary society and depression—for some 'moral siege' was clearly a way of maintaining morale. Many of those who were able to articulate well their critique of modern society seemed particularly well adjusted. For others, however, perhaps with a less sure grip on the rightness of their own values, change was deeply disturbing. This important theme of adjustment to old age in a changing society will be taken up later in the discussion of the case studies.

Subsequent History

Of the 76 people I originally visited, at the time of writing (14 years after I completed the data collection in 1971) three are still alive and living in the same sheltered housing schemes where I met them. Of the original sample, 17 moved out of the scheme where they were living, eight into residential care homes, seven into other independent housing schemes and two went to live with their daughters. As a whole, therefore, a very high proportion, certainly over three-quarters, remained living in sheltered housing until their deaths, either in the scheme or after a short stay in hospital (only one died on a long-stay hospital ward). Other studies in the same period have demonstrated the same low proportion of older people living in sheltered housing moving on into residential care homes (Boldy *et al.*, 1973). Certainly it was clear in this study that people were considerably disabled when they did make a move of this kind, and few survived this transition more than a short period, usually only a few months. Only two lived as long as two years when they moved to a residential home. Sheltered housing, therefore, does seem to allow people to retain their independence rather than encouraging a move to institutional living.

On the other hand, the short-term mortality rate of the sample was relatively high. There were five people in the sample whom I subsequently lost trace of, but of the 68 deaths I have recorded, 32 died within two years of the completion of my original study, i.e. by the end of 1973. Calculations show that over one-third and approaching one-half of the sample only lived in sheltered housing for a total period of three years or less. Contrasting those 32 who died after so short a stay from the 24 people who lived at least an additional three years more (i.e. they did not die before 1977) provides an opportunity to assess factors that might influence mortality. Those who died early were, not surprisingly, an older group (81 and 77 years median age respectively at the outset of the study). The other main observable differences between the two groups were in their health as recorded in 1971. The group that died earlier was a significantly frailer and more disabled group as measured by the Functional Health Index.

On the other indicators, however, differences were small. There was no difference in the incidence of recent widowhood and only small and insignificant differences in the mean level of depression scores. The same small but insignificant differences were reflected in the Life Satisfaction Index. There was no more or less criticism of present society among those who died earlier. There was, however, proportionately twice as much criticism of living in sheltered housing among those who died earlier rather than later. Although the numbers are small this is clearly a subject which warrants further investigation. It reflects the importance of the older person and others involved with them thinking carefully about the advantages and disadvantages of a move to sheltered housing.

In regard to problems with disability, physical frailty did increase with age in a number of people living in the scheme, and certainly one half of my sample was housebound in their last year in sheltered housing. However, considering the contemporary anxiety aroused by problems associated with dementia, it is worth recording that only four of the total sample of 71 I was able to follow up deteriorated mentally to a noticeable degree. Of these, two died very rapidly, and two moved into institutional care as a result. By comparison, problems associated with depression in over one-third of the sample, far outweighed dementia, and yet seemed to be rarely addressed by the health and welfare services. The issue of depression in certain members of the sample is discussed in detail in Chapter 7. As stressed in the previous chapter, maintenance of morale in old age is a key issue for gerontology, an issue of 'meaningful and purposeful existence' (Busse, 1985).

Chapter 4

Varying Attitudes to Reminiscence

Attitudes to Past Life and to Reminiscence

As described at the beginning of Chapter 3, a considerable amount of data was collected over a two-year period on each person's attitudes to his or her past life and to reminiscence. Measures of reminiscence characteristics were validated using independent assessors' ratings of conversation transcripts, as well as ratings of conversation characteristics obtained from the wardens of the sheltered housing schemes (Coleman, 1972). Besides the tape recorded and annotated conversations, responses to certain questionnaires (especially the Chicago Life Satisfaction Index and the Havighurst and Glasser Reminiscence Questionnaire) also provided relevant material.

The questions which most directly assessed attitudes to past life were six items on the Life Satisfaction Index: 'I have gotten more of the breaks in life than most of the people I know'; 'As I look back on my life I am fairly well satisfied'; 'I would not change my past life even if I could'; 'Compared to other people my age I've made a lot of foolish decisions in my life'; 'When I think back over my life I didn't get most of the important things I wanted'; and 'I've gotten pretty much what I expected out of life'. Separating these items from the rest of the scale was thought to have face validity and not to be inconsistent with the intentions of the scale's originators (Neugarten et al., 1961; Chown, 1977). Reflecting in large part Erikson's concept of 'integrity', these particular items were devised to measure the extent to which the individual both 'regards his life as meaningful and accepts resolutely that which life has been' and 'feels he has succeeded in achieving his major goals' (Neugarten et al., 1961).

The coherence of these 'past achievement' items has been borne out by both British and American research. In a study using the Life Satisfaction Index with 150 British men, Bigot was content to distinguish only two factors 'an affective assessment of the individual's present situation', and 'a judgement on achievement/fulfilment in regard to total life achievements' (Bigot, 1974). In the present study, too, factor analysis was employed on these items and the six afore-mentioned 'past' items formed a distinctly separate group. The value of this distinction has been borne out in recent research on older people suffering from psychiatric illness which noted that the 'past achievement' component of life

31

satisfaction appeared to be relatively stable over time, in contrast to present mood as assessed by items both from life satisfaction and depression scales (Gilleard *et al.*, 1981). It is worth noting, too, that in a recent review of research on the measurement of psychological well being, Lawton comments that 'congruence between desired and attained goals' is the only dimension to show up consistently as different investigators have factored the Life Satisfaction Index (Lawton, 1984).

Given that these items do appear to provide a valid assessment of satisfaction with past life, the question arises as to how the individuals interviewed in this study compared with people in other studies using the same scale. Over all their replies appeared as positive, and in some cases more positive than responses recorded in other studies. Of the sample 68 per cent gave predominantly positive responses to the six items taken as a whole. This is a higher figure than that reported in other studies with large samples of older people living in the Netherlands and in England, where comparable percentages of 53 per cent and 60 per cent with predominantly positive attitudes are cited (Coleman, 1983). The item with the highest satisfaction rating was 'As I look back on my life I am fairly well satisfied', with which 42 people (84 per cent) clearly agreed. The lowest rating was to the item 'When I think back over my life I didn't get most of the important things I wanted' with which only 25 (50 per cent) said they disagreed. Only on this item did responses appear more negative than data from other studies. For example Harris, in a nationwide stratified random sample of aged Americans, obtained a 61 per cent clear disagreement response to this item (Harris *et al.*, 1975).

Taken together, the results do seem to indicate that most people in later life reply to questioning about their past life with responses indicative of satisfaction. This is also consistent with other studies (Campbell *et al.*, 1976) which show that relative to younger individuals, older people score lower in present 'happiness' but higher in 'life satisfaction'. Certainly, this sample of people was no exception to this pattern, with relatively high past life satisfaction scores as compared with present morale.

Attitudes to reminiscence on the other hand, as assessed by the Havighurst and Glasser questionnaire, were much more variable. For example, only 24 (48 per cent) said they 'liked to think about the past', a much lower figure than the surveys of Dutch and English people referred to earlier, where figures of 68 per cent and 78 per cent were obtained (Coleman, 1983). A number referred to unpleasant feelings associated with reminiscence as well as to pleasant feelings.

The evidence on actual conversation was similarly mixed. There were clearly those who liked to reminisce and those who did not. With each individual I tape recorded certain conversations which I attempted to standardize by introducing the conversation in the same way to each person, and providing a minimal but regular input myself by asking specific questions. I said I was interested in the individual's views about past and present and began by asking whether the person found as he got older that he thought more about the past. When necessary, I continued to introduce questions as 'What kinds of things do you think about?'; 'Do you have any regrets?'; 'Do you try to make sense of it all?'; 'Does thinking about the past help you?'; 'Do you like to speak about old times?'; 'How does the past compare with the present?'; 'Can one learn from it?'. Where people did not appear eager to follow up reminiscing cues they were not pressed, and the conversation was supported more by cues about the individuals' present situation and their general attitudes to life around. In this kind of situation, and using one hour long recordings, 41 per cent of the conversation units were classified as reminiscence ones (i.e. pertaining to events of more than five years previous), with nine people (18 per cent) speaking for one-fifth or less of the conversation about the past and five people speaking for over two-thirds of the conversation about the past. That this provided quite a good measure of the individual's tendency to reminisce with me was shown by a very high correlation with a general rating I made of the amount the individual reminisced in all the conversations I rated over a two year period ($r = 0.82$). The level of association was also high with ratings made by the wardens of the sheltered housing schemes (Coleman, 1972). The questionnaire measure of interior reminiscing correlated at a lower but still significant level—0.40 with the tape recorded measure and 0.57 with the overall rating of amount of reminiscing in individuals' conversation.

Past Life Satisfaction and Morale

The devisors of the Life Satisfaction Index saw satisfaction with past life as a constituent of morale in old age (Neugarten *et al.*, 1961) and results consistently bear this out. In the present study a summed measure of the six 'past' life satisfaction items produced correlations of 0.27 with the remaining 14 'present' life satisfaction items and 0.25 with the MMPI Depression Scale (the latter two measures correlated together highly [$r = 0.77$]).

The basis of this relationship is worth considering. The literature on the subject when considered as a whole, would seem to suggest that the individual's satisfaction with the life he has led is something that increases with age and is then relatively impervious to change. Present happiness or mood state and its correlates such as self esteem and self rated health on the other hand, appear more vulnerable to the various losses of old age: loss of independence, loss of role and loss of close contacts. One might therefore hypothesize that the association that exists between past and present life satisfaction reflects the basic strength the individual is given in withstanding loss as a result of having a satisfactory life to look back on.

But this is not the only possibility. It may also be that the association rests on common links with the same determining factors, for instance in the individual's personality or social situation, or with intrinsically related factors. For example, present life circumstances could be in large measure the product of past life circumstances. A high income in younger life will tend to mean a good pension in old age. Marriage when young will tend to guarantee, for men at least, companionship in old age. In Dutch studies both present income and marital status have been found to be both independently and strongly associated with past life satisfaction (Coleman, 1983). People, therefore, who are satisfied with their present lives in old age will also tend to look favourably on related elements in their past lives.

The view implicit in the concept of 'integrity' and in much of the geronto-logical literature related to this subject suggests that satisfaction with past life has a positive influence in its own right. Those who feel they have lived their lives as they would have liked will be happier in the present as well. This is the concept of 'sense of fulfilment'. There are, however, as was seen in Chapter 2, two main strands of thought in the literature on this subject, one associated with the notion of 'life review' (Butler, 1963), the other with reminiscence as a means of maintaining identity.

Butler implied that the mental process of reviewing one's life is a universal experience in older persons. Often, as a result of this life review, negative ex-periences can be better understood, lessons are drawn from them and the person gains in the process. He or she feels more 'whole', develops a sense of peace, even of wisdom. But there is also the possibility of a negative outcome, a continuing obsession with certain events and actions, the lack of any 'solution' to them, and persisting feelings of guilt and depression. The relevance of this theory for the relationship between past life satisfaction and present adjustment is clear. It has common ground with Erikson's concept of development of ego integrity, and can be applied in therapy (Butler *et al.*, 1977). It should be noted that a number of other therapists also emphasize the importance of reflecting upon one's cumulative personal history as a task to be accomplished prior to death (for example, Frankl, 1963; Krasner, 1977; Blum and Tross, 1980).

However, more than the 'life review' theory, it is the 'identity maintenance' theory, the notion that a greater identification with past life and past achieve-ments is helpful to older people in situations of deprivation and loss, which seems to lie behind the present trend to promote 'reminiscence therapy' with groups of older people, especially those living in institutions (Help the Aged, 1981). The discrepancy between how one would like to live one's life and how one is actually leading it is minimized by stressing the value of the life that has already been lived, and that this in itself justifies a sense of self worth. Reminiscence therapy of course can also be seen as a tool, a ready means of promoting interest and engagement, provoking the traditional role of the older person as a 'storyteller', a preserver of memories (McMahon *et al.*, 1964).

Before turning to evidence from this study on the role of reminiscence in pro-moting morale, it is worth pointing out that there is a third possible explanation of the relationship between past and present life satisfaction in which present experience influences past memories. That memories are coloured by current mood is a well documented phenomenon. An interesting example in the geronto-logical literature is a study by Tobin and Etigson (1968) of older people moving to live in institutions. They demonstrated a significant increase in 'loss' themes, (for example separation experience, threat of injury, illness, mutilation, death) when they were asked to describe their earliest memories after moving to the institution, compared with before. No change was shown in a matched sample of people who remained living in the community. An important observation in the literature on depression also is 'retrospective generalization' (Beck, 1976), whereby the person generalizes from one negative event or behaviour to many other unrelated events or behaviours. 'When elderly persons are depressed in the present, they tend to generalize into the past. Thus, many or most relationships and events in their pasts are viewed negatively because of present depressogenic thinking, when in fact those things in the past were not really negative' (Sherman, 1981, p. 231). However, it should be noted that the evidence for as high past life satisfaction in institutionalized as in non-institutionalized older people would indicate that the influence of present situation on perception of the past cannot be so pervasive a phenomenon.

It is also possible to argue that the same phenomenon could operate in a positive direction. A person whose life has worked out comfortably, will perhaps be less inclined at the end to be critical of his past. The basic underlying phenomenon is one of cognitive consistency and the diminution of dissonant thoughts and feelings (Festinger, 1957). The same ideas underly therapeutic work designed to promote a more salient and positive self concept of oneself in the past. This will inevitably, it is thought, tend to produce a more positive self concept in the present (Lewis, 1973).

Reminiscence and Morale

In the present study, small but generally insignificant correlations between the various measures of reminiscence and the measures of physical and social loss gave some slight support to the view that reminiscing may appear as a consequence of environmental change or a threat of environmental change in old age (see Lieberman and Falk, 1971), but, just as Lieberman's data, they provided little if any support to the hypothesis that reminiscence *per se* is a markedly adaptive response. There were no associations with measures of morale even when taking the level of loss incurred into account.

From a detailed analysis of relationships between the various conversation measures and measures of adjustment (Coleman, 1972, 1974), the one result to stand out concerned the measure of 'life review' conversation, based on recordings of the extent of the conversation devoted to psychological, analytical and evaluative comments on the person's past life. There was a strong (almost) statistically significant) association with dissatisfaction with past life as might be expected, and most strikingly those eight people who were both dissatisfied with their past lives but did little or no 'life reviewing' in their conversation, had significantly lower morale than the rest of the group. Life reviewing therefore appeared adaptive for people who were dissatisfied with their pasts.

It was also noteworthy that general informative and attitudinal conversation about the world, whether employing past or present material, was related to high morale in the men in the sample, but not the women.

A more differentiated consideration of reminiscence therefore seems essential. It is clear that speaking about the past can vary a great deal in content and in function. Where the individual was dissatisfied with some aspect of their life and discussed it openly, reminiscence clearly had quite a different character to where, for example, he or she was using the past to tell entertaining or instructive stories. Such differences in the use of reminiscence were expressed by the people themselves when asked for their attitudes to reminiscence both on the Havighurst and Glasser questionnaire and in general conversation, whether for example they found it a 'pleasurable' or 'unpleasurable' activity and the kinds of 'purposes' it fulfilled. Their own comments were very revealing and seem to provide the best basis for seeking to explore further the nature of reminiscence.

The first point to note is whether they regarded themselves as reminiscers. On the questionnaire they were asked to what extent they had thought back on the past over the last couple of weeks, 'a great deal', 'some' or 'very little'. The sample was very evenly divided on this question and this in itself demonstrates the value of speaking of 'reminiscers' and 'non-reminiscers' as Lewis did in his experimental work on reminiscence (Lewis, 1971). Seventeen people said they reminisced very little or not at all, 15 said some and 18 said they reminisced a great deal. There was a clear association between reminiscence and past life satisfaction in that 14 of the 18 people who reminisced a great deal expressed clear satisfaction with their past life, whereas only nine out of the 17 who said they reminisced very little did the same. But the fact that there were notable exceptions in both directions—both those who reminisced a great deal who were dissatisfied and those who reminisced very little who were very satisfied—shows the past life satisfaction does not provide a complete explanation of variations in reminiscence.

Among those who said they reminisced a great deal, all saw reminiscence as something they did a lot of now in later life and more than earlier in life. But when they were asked to describe its characteristics and the functions it served for them, there was a clear split in the group. Fourteen people described reminiscence in wholly positive terms as giving them 'a good feeling', gaining for them 'appreciation of their life', or 'a sense of fulfilment', and helping them in 'making sense of things'. A number said it was also 'a comfort', a help in 'getting over difficulties', although four people said it was not sufficient help in coping with the present difficulties they were currently facing. The remaining four people, however, who reminisced a lot, described it in quite different terms. One man said that he 'argued' with himself and that some of his thoughts were 'terrible'. Another said that thoughts about the past obsessed him and 'drove him mad'. The other two spoke about troubling thoughts. One said 'there is nothing harder than the past'. These four seemed to be involved in an active life review process in which they were confronting parts of their life which they found difficult to accept.

Among those who said they reminisced very little, a similarly evident split in attitudes appeared. The majority, 13 people, expressed themselves more or less neutrally, saying that reminiscence was of little or no help or had 'no point or purpose'. But the remaining four expressed a much more disturbed attitude to reminiscence, stating or implying that they personally had to avoid thinking about the past because it made their present situation worse. Comments were made as 'it makes me feel more miserable', 'it gives me a sad feeling', 'it makes it harder for me to bear this life', 'it makes it more difficult for me to accept the present'.

It was not difficult to place the remaining 15 people who said they reminisced to some degree, within this basic four-fold distinction (see below)—whether they valued reminiscence, were troubled by unhappy memories, saw no point in reminiscing or had to avoid it. Of the 15, seven had a predominantly positive attitude to reminiscence as an enjoyable activity which brought them a sense of appreciation of their life, four stressed the regretful and hurtful nature of their memories, two saw reminiscence as a minor activity which had no relevance to their present situation and a further two saw reminiscence as something they really would prefer to avoid because comparison with the present was too depressing. Altogether then, 21 people in the sample could be described as valuing their memories, eight people as having disturbed memories, 15 as seeing no point in reminiscing and six people as having to avoid reminiscing because of the sense of loss it produced in them. Not surprisingly, the second and fourth groups had significantly lower morale than the first and third groups. Six of the eight people who were disturbed by reminiscence that they could not avoid, were depressed according to the definition given in the last chapter, and of those who felt they had to avoid reminiscence because the comparison with the past made them sad, five were depressed.

Although as already indicated, there is some evidence that this sample contained a higher than average proportion of people who did not enjoy reminiscing, the distinctions that have been drawn seem inherently interesting and worth exploring further. They also help explain why neither the tendency to reminisce or not to reminisce is likely to be associated with morale. Both reminiscence and non-reminiscence can be expressed positively and negatively. Reminiscence can be an encouraging and/or comforting activity, but it can also be a worrying and disturbing process. Similarly, not reminiscing can be purposeful because there are better things to do. But it can also be avoidance of memories of a past that overshadow the present and that heighten the experience of loss.

TABLE 1: TYPES OF ATTITUDES TO REMINISCENCE AND RELATED MORALE

Reminiscers:	Value memories of past (n = 21)	High morale
	Troubled by memories of past (n = 8)	Low morale
Non-Reminiscers:	See no point in reminiscing (n = 15)	High morale
	Have to avoid because of contrast past and present (n = 6)	Low morale

These are the distinctions I wish to examine further in the rest of this book.

Longitudinal Case Studies

In the following chapters I wish to consider the reminiscences and the attitudes to reminiscence of the people in each of these four groups as they described them to me when I first met them, and as they related to the individual's adjustment. I have also recorded any changes in reminiscence and adjustment over the ensuing years. Rather than describe statistical evidence on each group I have chosen to focus on a few individuals and describe their attitudes in some detail. I have done this mainly because I believe it is only possible at present to address the complex issues involved at the level of the individual case. It is a great pity that psychologists by and large have neglected the value of the individual case study in their haste to proceed to derive general principles of human behaviour. It may be that the patient application of 'quasi-judicial' methods to reach conclusions on individual adjustment, and the gradual development thereby of 'case law' (Bromley, 1978, 1986) will show better results in the long run. It is also likely to make more interesting reading, which is a second reason for proceeding in this way.

I have selected for case studies those people on whom I collected the most evidence. These were all people who survived at least four years after my initial study (i.e. beyond 1975) and whom I visited a number of times over that period of time and whom I felt I got to know well enough to justify the compilation of such case studies. This had a disadvantage of emphasizing the 'survivor' effect, that is focussing the study on those who lived longer than others, and this must be acknowledged. But I have also included brief evidence on the lives of the other people in the study as a check on any conclusions that I have reached from analysing in detail only a few cases.

Seven of the studies are of people who were still alive in 1981 when I interviewed in depth using the same methodology as ten years previously, i.e. the same questionnaires and interview procedures. In some cases too I also repeated tape recorded conversations. These cases therefore include more substantial evidence on reminiscence in a longitudinal perspective.

In Chapter 9 I have grouped together the case studies on three individuals, two who presented as reminiscers and one who did not, who seemed to exemplify highly successful modes of adjustment to life despite considerable physical difficulties and social isolation, and who made the greatest impression on me personally. Again it is not customary for social researchers to demonstrate personal interest, but in the case of research of this nature I think it is inevitable and probably desirable. As part of the total sum of material which needs to be considered in assessing the validity of the conclusions that have been reached, it is important to lay also one's own personal impressions and biases on the table. It is the value of the objective evidence that we are judging, but researchers are inevitably vehicles for the evidence they present on individual cases and should be prepared to be open about how they have experienced people and perhaps been moved by them. This may be helpful to others trying to assess the value of the same evidence. In each case study I have not hesitated to describe my own reactions where they seemed to me to be relevant.

Each case study then focusses on the relationship between the individual's attitudes to reminiscence and the nature of his or her personal adjustment, and all salient information that I collected relevant to this theme is included. In presenting each case I have tried to follow a similar structure. Initially I have set out a summary of the information I collected on the individuals' life history and life-style and have described and illustrated their attitudes to and characteristics of reminiscence when we first met. I have examined possible relationships between these attitudes and their present state of adjustment to their life situations, noting what significance was being given to reminiscence. I have also noted any comments that reflected on attitudes to society as a whole, as material on these attitudes was usually available and because they appear to be an important element in over-all adjustment in later life, as stressed in the last chapter. I have also noted any other striking features that emerged from general conversation. I have have then considered the evidence collected over the ensuing years and drawn conclusions, where they appeared justified, regarding whether attitudes in all these various respects had remained the same or changed over the subsequent years, and how change or otherwise was related to people's state of adjustment.

The use of a case study method of research requires considerable co-operation on the part of the subjects of the study. This is one reason for its unpopularity as a method. For it is necessary not only to explain the purpose of the enquiry and to obtain consent, but to secure continued co-operation often for a series of detailed interviews. All 50 people described in this book agreed to be the subjects for the original reminiscence study, and the 14 who are the subjects of the case studies were all people whom I learned to know well and liked, and who knew of my intentions to write a book based on their lives. (The names used in this book are of course fictitious.)

The question arises though whether in research of this nature, where substantial conclusions are being drawn about the course of individuals' lives, more involvement in the actual presentation of results should be sought.Individuals could, for example, be invited to comment on the conclusions drawn on them and present their own perspectives. This has not been done in the present study, but I think that it would have been enriched by such a procedure. However, as part of the standard method of presentation I have adopted for each case study, I have given considerable weight to presenting the individuals' views in their own words where possible.

Chapter 5

Valuing Memories

Distinguishing Characteristics

The first group of people clearly distinguishable in their attitudes to reminiscing, comprised 21 out of the 50 people in the study. They were those who indicated that reminiscence played a significant and positive part in their lives. They varied in the degree of emphasis they gave to reminiscence but all said they regarded their memories as a valuable possession, even with and sometimes because of the difficulties they had had. Interestingly, a number said to me that they could and would like to write a book about their lives! For that reason they were particularly interested in the book they thought I would write about them. The group included individuals for whom the past in general was seen as preferable to the present and therefore they were glad they had lived in an earlier period. But most of the group were not concerned with this comparison, but simply gained a great deal psychologically from remembrances of happy times and achievements.

Most were well adjusted, but few if any had had easy lives. They referred a lot to coping with and learning from difficulties. Mrs Parsons for example described experiencing her life now as 'a pattern, all rolled out behind her'. She had learned from the difficulties in her life and now felt a 'wiser' person. Many were proud they had overcome difficulties, and not been overwhelmed by them. Mr Turner had been through difficulties in the First World War, in service together with his wife afterwards and then bringing up his daughter on his own when his wife died young in the 1920s. He had a high self esteem, both based on his achievements in the past where he had been 'a bit of a rebel'—he had once been sacked from his job as a gardener for giving away apples that were lying on the ground to an orphanage—and in the present where he 'kept going' doing gardening and other jobs for people despite his advanced age of 88 years. He was a lively talker and had a lot of stories to tell about his past life. Mr Locke was similar in the importance he attributed to 'self help' and keeping one's independence. He was virtually blind when I met him but remarkably cheerful. A policeman during the Second World War and subsequently a school caretaker, he spoke about his life in an undramatic way, stressing the bright periods, even during the Second World War, despite the fact that he had lost his first wife in a bombing raid. 'There was much humour too in the war,' he said.

Mr French was especially proud of his army links which connected both past and present. He had wanted to join the cavalry from a young boy and he was glad he had been able to fulfil this wish. Ideally he would like to be at 'Chelsea', at the Royal Hospital and Home for Retired Soldiers. He was chairman of the local branch of the Old Contemptibles and despite his disability looked forward to his attendance at the annual dinner. Mr Dennis's reminiscences too concerned the army. His childhood had been unhappy but his life had 'taken a turn for the better' when he joined the army. He reminisced a lot about his army days, particularly in Ireland at the time of the 'troubles' in the 1920s. He had married an Irish wife and become a Roman Catholic. His subsequent married life had been a very happy one, and he greatly looked forward to his regular trips to Ireland to stay with relatives of his dead wife. A number of other men spoke about experiences in the First World War, whereas others still focussed much more on their subsequent careers, their ambitions and their achievements.

The women by contrast spoke much more about family life. There were five women in particular who dwelt a great deal on childhood, their parents, and the delights of family life in the past. Mrs Bedford spoke vividly about her country childhood, of the pleasures and the freshness of life then. 'Now I'm back there ... I see things hanging in the room.' Not one of the men spoke about childhood to the extent that these five women did. Other women spoke a lot about life with their husbands, and some of their careers as well. Miss Jansen said she had a feeling of having had a worthwhile life thinking of all the children she had been nanny to. Born in Denmark, she had come to England to go into service after her mother died in 1898.

The characteristic that united them all was a pleasure in looking back on their past lives. A number—including some of the oldest men—expressed a nostalgic sense of how quickly life had gone:

'... looking back the 1914 war seems to have been only about five or six years ago.'

'... as the Bible says, even if you live a thousand years it's like you'd lived one day when the time comes to die. I certainly feel it's gone so quick ...'

A small sub-group of four people, although expressing positive attitudes to their memories, found these to be of insufficient help in coping with their present difficulties. All were depressed, and in all cases there were very specific objects or causes of their depression. Mr Pym was severely handicapped by pain. He had cancer of the stomach although he had not yet been told. Mr Laver was unable to move far after a severe stroke. Miss Trickett was going blind and did not feel at home in the sheltered housing scheme she had come to. Mrs Somerton had not yet been able to get over the loss of her husband five years previously. She had a history of depressive reactions to loss. Though depressed, they did admit that the past was of some comfort to them. After the early death of his wife, Mr Laver had brought up their five sons on his own. They had once given him a cup for being 'the best dad'. At the same time it was striking how many stories of 'loss' he had to tell: how he had lost his money to welshers at the Epsom Derby day when the suffragette had thrown herself under the King's horse; how he had been kicked in the face by a horse while he was going on his milk round; how he had hurt his jaw in a cycle accident; how he had seen a severed woman's head on the bumpers of a train; how fooling around with his wife he had seen her fall back on the cooker and hurt herself (which he thought could have been the cause of her cancer). His memories seem to illustrate how the choice of reminiscences can reflect the experiences of present loss, as demonstrated in the study by Tobin and Etigson (1968) of institutionalized elderly people in the USA. Mrs Somerton, too, had many stories to tell of the personal losses she had suffered in her life, though she, as Mr Laver, had a predominantly happy life to look back on.

Miss Trickett said that she 'lived in the past'. Such a form of expression has been shown by the survey studies referred to in the previous chapter, both in the Netherlands and in England, to be indicative of low morale. As Miss Trickett said, she had 'no interest in the present'. For the majority of people who valued their memories on the other hand, the past served more to give or to keep an interest in the present, in applying its lessons and standards, for example, in family life or in maintaining the threads of continuity. Mr Pym was still relatively young at 72 and greatly missed contact with other people. Only a few years previously he had still been helping his wife in a café and been working occasionally as a bus driver. His medical condition which gave him pain and continuous diarrhoea made going out difficult and his depressed state was very understandable.

A number of people did compare past with present ways of life. A theme raised by many for example was that material progress did not necessarily bring greater contentment. Mr Turner addressed the question to me: 'Are you happier with your car than I was with my bike?' Others echoed the same point.

'Well I think they have a lot of things now that we never had, but they are no happier with it. It's like the man with the motor. He starts with a small car then he wants a bigger one ... especially the young people, they get dissatisfied. They want a better car and a better car ...'

'... if I was to make her up a little rag doll like we used to have in the country—we used to get a lump of wood and put some material round it, then make a little head, tie its neck around—she thinks the world of that, more than if you gave her a 25 shilling doll that we gave her at Christmas.'

'... there's nothing for them to have when they get a bit older, they've had it all. They've had it all in their childhood.'

Comparing this group with the sample as a whole, however, it is important to stress that their positive attitudes to reminiscence did not mean that their attitudes to the present were any more negative. Eight of the 21 people in this group had what could be described as relatively tolerant attitudes to present society, compared with ten out of 29 in the rest of the sample (i.e. the balance of negative to positive comments on the present was no greater for those who valued their memories). Therefore it seems fair to conclude that individuals often valued their past experience in its own right, and not simply by comparison with today.

Two striking examples of a tolerant and unprejudiced attitude to present society combined with a highly positive valuation of the individual's personal experience will be presented in Chapter 9. Two of the three case studies presented in this chapter, however, and one in particular, combine an extremely positive evaluation of past time in conjunction with a critical attitude to the present. It is important to consider such a combination of attitudes, already referred to in Chapter 3 as 'moral siege'. But it would be wrong to consider it an inevitable combination. The cases presented in Chapter 9 demonstrate that a high value given to past memories does not preclude an optimistic view of the present and the future.

The three cases described in this chapter exemplify three different styles and objects of reminiscing. For Miss Smith the old days are the 'good old days' and she delights in praising them and drawing out contrasts with the present. She conveys the sense that it might be possible to put the clock back. Therefore, she sees her reminiscences as serving a useful purpose. For Mr Austin, experiences of the First World War dwarf all the other memories he possesses. He is a compulsive reminiscer of what he observed in those few years, and he struggles still to see the war in proper focus. He can see no sense in it. But his awareness that he has been part of history gives him a strong sense of identity, and a feeling of amazement too that he has survived to live so long. Mr Cook was fortunate to do a job in life that he greatly enjoyed. He would have liked it to have continued for as long as possible. In reminiscing and in other ways he prolongs his work identity as a tugman.

All three provide an instructive element to their reminiscences, Miss Smith in particular. The story telling element is strong in each of their reminiscences too, perhaps most evident in Mr Cook's conversation. Life review elements occur too and 'myth making', especially in Miss Smith's accounts of the past ('we had the real food'). Mr Austin by contrast appears fearlessly objective in recording his experiences of the First World War. The most important common feature they all share is a strong connection between their reminiscences and their present sense of self, an experience of continuity based in the very solid reality of their past lives. Mr Austin says that he has to 'shake himself' in order to believe that he has survived the war, but the war itself was real enough. To deny the importance of that past to their present life would seem absurd to them. It gives them a vital depth and a strength in the present.

Miss Smith

I remember Miss Smith as an excitable, almost bubbling, person who greatly enjoyed entertaining me and telling me about her life. She was interested that I was 'writing a book' based on conversations with old people and every time I

saw her she would ask me how it was going. She had been born in 1882—and so
was already 88 when I first met her—the last of eight children in the family. Her
father died when she was five as the result of an accident in which he was run
over by a haywain; other sections of the family had misfortune too. One uncle
had been deported to Australia for sheep stealing, and yet another drowned in
the local water works! Yet Miss Smith's memories of childhood were very happy
ones. Her mother had gone to work from six in the morning until six in the
evening, and under her 'guiding hand' all had gone well. All Miss Smith's
brothers and sisters had played their part.

'...one would get the fire going, one would chop some wood and me being the youngest
would do something else, then when mother came home there was the tea... My mother
would go up the shops on the way home, she'd bring in some chops or she'd bring in some
steak, or what she would do is she would go and get six pennies worth of pieces, beef
pieces and some kidney and she'd make us a nice stew, or she'd make a nice pudding,
meat pudding, ... they don't have things like that now! ...'

Miss Smith remembered how her mother told the children they must 'always
make up before night'. There had been 'wonderful Christmases'. She thought of
her mother with a special pride and love, for very understandable reasons.

'I remember my mother telling me as we got older, we were all sitting round the table, that
was after my father died ... I was about five, my two brothers, two of my sisters, and a
lady came in, she was what they called the district visitor... she said, "Oh Mrs Smith, why
don't you let one or two of your children go into Barnado's Home". My mother looked
round the table, she thought which one can I spare. "I can't spare any of them," she said,
"No, I'll never part with one. While we've got a crust of bread we'll share it, but I cannot
part with one of my children."... We never lost pride, we still kept that pride, we still kept
a clean home, it was poor but it was clean and it was happy.'

While her mother lived—and her mother lived till the age of 93—there was
always a room for Miss Smith at her house.

Miss Smith worked for most of her life in service, learning first to be a nanny
at the age of 13. Her longest lasting position had been for 42 years in the house of
a Presbyterian minister. After his death she had remained as companion to his
wife. She was paid little but travelled a lot and had 'wonderful times'. She
became a very close friend of her employer.

The hardest part of Miss Smith's life was to come in fact after she was 75. With
her friend's death in 1957, Miss Smith became depressed. She went to live with a
widowed brother who had always been her favourite brother, but could not
cope. Help, however, came to her in a variety of ways. Her old friend had left her
an annuity of three pounds a week but also an envelope ...

'One day we were sitting there, she gave me an envelope, she said Edi I want you to have
this, but promise me that you won't open it unless you absolutely need it, as if to say,
suppose you're not well and you've got to go away, something like that. Well I put that
envelope away, I didn't open it ...'

With the £40 that was in this envelope her bank manager arranged for her to find a place in a nursing home where she recovered from her 'nervous breakdown'.

More difficulties were to come, however, five years later, when her brother died after a long illness, virtually penniless, and she couldn't afford to continue living in the accommodation he had rented. She had hoped that she could go and live with another of her brothers, but 'bad friends' advised him against doing this and she was left with nowhere to go. She 'did not know what to do'. But again help came in the form of the bank manager, the vicar and her old employer's son. They all made efforts to find new housing for her, and a nephew took her to live with him for a while. Eventually she was found a room in a terrace block of housing newly converted by the district council into a sheltered housing scheme. This is where I met her.

Here she was very happy. She 'loved' the room and enjoyed the other people around. She was full of interest too for all the happenings in the families of her various nephews and nieces, whom she saw regularly.

Memories of her past life, however, were the major features of her conversation, and she needed little encouragement to tell me about them. She was concerned especially to stress how good things had been in the past, in her childhood for instance.

'When we were at school we used to have some good times, because we all used to play in together, not like the children now. We used to be, of course, working in school but we had much better lessons that fitted us for things that we were going to be able to do. For instance, we used to work for examinations, we used to have to do a bit of sewing, a bit of knitting, a bit of sort of crochet, and then when examination time came round, it was all sewn on a bit of paper... I'll show you a sample that my sister worked at the school, it's over a hundred years old ...'

'We were far happier in those days than they are now. They were large families, well mother couldn't give every one of those children something, but she'd buy one thing, perhaps she'd buy a packet of sweets or she'd give us so much, four pence, to go up the shop and buy half a pound of sweets, but then we'd share them, but they don't now, nobody shares with you now, nobody gives you anything now, even the grown ups they don't share...'

'... In the summer, we used to go to Sunday School and we used to go for a treat, but we didn't used to go like they go now, we used to go for a ride in a haycart! We used to think it was lovely, and we used to have a mug of tea and perhaps a cake or something like that. We had a good time, a better time than ever they have now!'

'... Children have got no idea of playing by themselves today. No idea. We used to play hopscotch, we'd come home from school, change our shoes, put on our old shoes, make a square and play hopscotch ... Then on a Saturday or a Sunday, mother used to take us for a walk, big sisters used to go with us, perhaps we'd take some tea in a bottle or something like that, go up the park, go to Sunday School but no not now, they don't behave like that.'

Her memories gave her a strong sense of having been fortunate.

'I often sit here and I think to myself what a happy time we had in those days. They think now they are having such a wonderful time, and they think oh I'm glad we didn't live in those ages, but oh, they don't know what they have missed! We grew up kind and thoughtful and if you could help anybody you did. If anybody was hard up a mother would go and do for her, and that mother would come in for her if ever her children weren't well.'

Many things about the present disturbed her, in particular problems resulting from children being 'pampered' when young and later going astray, problems also with 'wicked' strikes. She had recently had personal experience of difficulties in her own family, with the divorce of the son of her niece brought about as she saw it by 'bad company and drugs'. Such problems on a widespread scale were something new. She asked herself, 'What's going to happen? What's it going to be like? ... What would mother say? ... she would want to go back to sleep!'

Her criticism of the present extended even to nutrition.

'Children of today will not grow up to be as old as I am. I was brought up on nourishing substantial food, they are brought up on tins before and after they are born. Well now my niece came here with the baby... and I said, "What are you going to give the baby, Margaret?". "Oh," she said, "I brought her dinner with me, I brought my saucepan, I brought everything." She sterilized some stuff out of a tin. I said, "What's that?". Now it was Robinson's baby food, it was something she had got. She said, "She'll have this first and then she'll have something else, some sort of pudding after that". She had not had her dinner five minutes before she brought it all up. "Oh Margaret," I said, "is that what you feed your baby on?" "Oh, yes," she said, "Aunty, that's wonderful dinner," she said, "she had meat and I don't know what she didn't have in that first lot, and that's her afters." I said, "Oh, good gracious me I couldn't eat it," I said, "good job she has not seen it, to understand what she is eating. Oh dear," I said, "what did our mothers do?" I said, "In fact what did your mother do?" I said, "Your mother never gave you that." I said, "Our mothers went and got so much shin of beef and made some nice beef tea, or our mothers went and got a scrag end of mutton and made some nice mutton stew". I said, "You'd give her that?" Well, that baby at six months and with that food, she is not going to make the bone that has been made in me, the blood and the flesh that's been made in me, is it? Those children are not going to grow up strong healthy people and live long like us. We had the real food, didn't we, and that's why we old people are reaping the benefit of it now...'

'Another little niece, the youngest one of those two over there, she came here with her mother. "Doesn't the dinner smell good," she said. I got some scrag end of mutton, I put some barley in it, onion, carrots and some nice dumplings and made a nice rice pudding and some stewed apples. After she had had her dinner, she said, "Oh Mum," she said, "I've never had dinner like that before," she said, "I have enjoyed that dinner, that's a lovely dinner, oh I'll go to Aunty," she said, "that was a nice dinner"...'

Her reminiscences contained a number of elements of self justification. She criticized the present generation for being spoiled, for 'getting money too easy' and still being dissatisfied. She had been satisfied with little, and she had been rewarded for it.

'Did I tell you about my little niece, about what she said about Christmas? About what a silly Christmas when I told her all the things we used to do, how we had a Christmas tree and used to put all these things on the Christmas tree, make handkerchief satchels. "What a soppy Christmas!" she said. She was only about seven or eight. "What a soppy Christmas!" I said, "a far better Christmas than you have now, we were happy, now all you think about is what you are going to get." They way she said it! And I was telling her about the beautiful Christmases that we had, and we used to have tops and all these things. And now I can knit, I can sew, I can make cakes and I can do everything, whereas they go down the shop and buy them. And I am far happier.'

She didn't agree that she had been paid too little in life, and should have asked for more money from her employer. She felt justified by the events that followed.

'All those 42 years I had the lowest wage there was, I was happy, I had a good home, the lady was kind, nobody could have been kinder than Mr and Mrs Knott were to me... I never had much money, but that lady, I'd go away with that lady, she'd give me a holiday, I'd go to all different places with her, where I would never have gone, however much money I would have had, you see. When she died she left me £500 to buy an annuity and it was to amount to the same as when I was working for her, that was £3 a week... And her family made that money up to buy that annuity for £3 a week. Mr Knott's son is 70 now, he comes here to see me once a month, he brought me that plant, and he is kindness itself. Well supposing I had clamoured for more money where would I have been now. I was content with what I was having ...'

Her criticisms of the present, however, never led her to make bitter remarks. Her contentment with her own life was genuine.

I saw Miss Smith ten times over the following five years. She remained very much the same—always enthusiastic to see me—and having a great interest in the welfare of her family and those around her. The upheavals she had suffered before finding a place in sheltered housing were behind her. Now life 'went on smoothly'. When I last saw her, she has just bought a carpet and a small refrigerator with money she had been given as presents. She was delighted with them. She was planning holidays to visit various relatives. She died a couple of years later at the age of 97, by all accounts remaining very much the same until the last year when she became suddenly frail and was taken into care in an old people's home, where she died soon afterwards.

Miss Smith was someone for whom reminiscence played a valuable function. Her happy memories predominated over the unhappy ones and she enjoyed thinking back. She enjoyed also telling other people about them. Her criticism of the present was tempered by genuine concern which must have made others warm to her even if they disagreed. She felt she had a duty to tell people how good things had been in the past. Maybe they would learn from it!

Had reminiscence helped her in her trials in her late seventies when she lost two homes and two people to whom she was attached, first a companion of 40 years and then her favourite brother? In those times she had been able to recall examples of resourcefulness from the past, from her mother in particular, and from the belief her mother had conveyed to her that where there was a will there was a way. Closely associated too was her religious faith. In her difficulties she had prayed that 'God would give her strength'. At a particularly difficult moment her vicar had prayed too with her 'for strength and courage and faith and trust' and she had found people enough around her whom she could trust and who wanted to help her.

No one could deny her right to feel especially happy. Her past and present happiness were inextricably linked.

'Now wasn't I happy with that little bit of money that I was earning? Aren't I happier now to sit in my nice little room and think to myself and look back on those happy memories, ... No one could look back like I do could they?'

Mr Austin

Mr Austin was also in his late eighties when I first got to know him. He had been a widower for ten years. He was now beginning to feel frail as he couldn't do the jobs he was used to, like decorating and gardening. He said he had slowed down a lot in the last two years, and was 'getting past it, worst luck'. A quiet man with sensitive, soulful eyes, he would nevertheless speak with great animation on his experiences in the First World War, experiences that obviously still lived strongly within him. I visited and spoke with him on four occasions in 1971 and 1972, and each time the war dominated his conversation.

Mr Austin's early life had not been a happy one. His mother had died when he was very young, and his father married again. He said he could remember nothing of his childhood days. He spoke almost as an orphan.

'...I battled through it, I was on my own, my sister went away and left me and I was on my own when I was 14, I had to fight my way through the world.'

He regretted his lack of education in particular, but as a result was especially proud of the education he had been able to give his own son and the profitable use he had made of it.

He had started in the same trade as his father, the building trade, but he had soon left home and gone into lodgings. He had worked for various firms in his life, the longest period in a candle factory. He had been out of work three times, but had always been lucky to find work again quickly. He had married in 1912, when he was in his late twenties and a baby son had been born the year later. His wife was not able to have more children. He did not speak much to me about his wife and son, but expressed a great happiness about his married life. Life had never been the same, he said, since his wife died. His son was a 'good boy' and he saw him regularly once or twice a month. But he missed work. He hadn't wanted to retire at 65, but had had 'to make room for others'.

In his conversation about the past, however, it was the First World War that he came back to time and again. He had been called up to military service in 1914, and had gone right through the war. He had been made a machine gunner at the outset and had been part of the big events recorded in the history books. He had been there when the disastrous attack was made on the strong German positions at the Somme in 1916.

'I was on the Somme for three months . . . when we tried to take Vimy Ridge . . . five days' solid bombardment from every gun they'd got . . . then we had orders to go over . . . the East Surreys, the Fusiliers, the Lincolnshires, were all wiped out. . . the Germans were all down in the dug-outs, 60 feet dug-outs. They came out all along the parapets of the trenches, they all had machine guns fixed . . . it was like hail stones, it was like they were mowing down corn.'

A year later he took part in the equally terrible events at Ypres. He saw the blowing up of the Messines Ridge after months of secret work by the mining companies had driven galleries under the German positions.

'. . . I went down to see it, and they took us over to see this tunnel, to see what they were doing. They had railways down there, bringing up all the rubble and muck, mud and water, on trucks . . . and of course they blew this ridge up. They blew the whole hill up, you see, and stopped them having the view across. Blew all the ground up. It was terrific, the dynamite, yes they had dug a 100 feet down and they blew it all up. A horrible part, that was . . .'

He shared in the hopeless fighting afterwards to gain a few miles of quagmire.

'I was on the Passchendaele Ridge there. We had tanks there. They all got bogged down. Mud and water. They couldn't do nothing. The men died in the tanks there, they did. We were the third division to go up in support. The reserves and the 8th Brigade, they went over at five o'clock in the morning. Reports come through to the headquarters that we took the first line and second line and the third line of the German trenches, and at half past four in the afternoon the Brigadier came down and he said, "Get yourselves ready, you've got to go over," as we were the reserves, you see, we were the 8th Brigade. It was daylight mind you, oh we didn't have a ghost of a chance, the shell holes were all full of water. . . well there were only six of us came out of our company, six of us out of 36. . . we didn't get out of it until the evening. The Brigadier said the next morning, he said, "Well if the ground had been a bit hard there wouldn't have been a man jack come back". So it was too, because half the shells didn't explode, they went into the mud and never exploded. Good job too!'

He survived on to 1918 and the final attempt by the Germans, now with superior numbers, following the transfer of men from the Eastern front after the Russian collapse, to strike a knock-out blow before the fresh American man-power could tip the balance in the other direction.

'. . . I was on sentry that morning, the 21st March . . . and I heard a big explosion, oh I thought our boys have caught a German gun and it's gone up . . . and then the head-quarters ran a gas masks alert . . . it was all gas for four hours it was, we couldn't see a thing, of course it drove us right back . . . we didn't get it quite so bad as they did on the right . . . we had to lay quiet there. Not a word, not a rifle to be shot or anything, and in the evening they got us out of it, I don't know how, but they got us out. We went right back about a couple or three miles back. The French froggies and the Belgians were digging new trenches for us to go into ... it was only a storm that saved us really, a heavy storm set in, stopped Jerry getting his guns up. He couldn't get his guns up because of the water and the rain and the mud. It was lucky really in that respect, else we couldn't have stopped them...'

He was part also of the final advance to victory a few months later and was wounded only three weeks before the declaration of peace.

'... I'd gone all through it up until then ... every division went over that morning, every division in the field, Australians, New Zealanders, the lot ... we were organizing the troops to make new trenches and we were there talking, I had my machine gun on my shoulder, and there must have been a Jerry in a shell hole somewhere. I said, "You bloody fool," I swore, "you're killing your own men". See there must have been a Jerry in a shell hole ... must have been hand grenades all tied in a bundle, we all got put out of action, a lot got killed, I got knocked down. I didn't know where my machine gun went, but I got seriously wounded in the thigh, broken elbow, terrible state I was in ...'

Nevertheless, the sense of how lucky he had been to survive all that killing was almost overwhelming for him. Once he said he 'ought to have been dead years ago'. So many others, including his friends, had died.

'Oh I think heaps of times how I got through it and my old pals got killed. I lost two of my mates that went with me into the regiment who I'd been with about two months. One died in my arms ... I'd got him in my arms, but before I could get the dressing out to dress his wounds he'd passed away, and I said to the officer, what shall I do with him. He said well shove him in the front bunk hole, take his pay book—that's all they thought of you. Couldn't do nothing about it, they couldn't help themselves... Yes, my mates, the Kingston boys, got killed. I was lucky really, I got clouted at the finish admittedly, but I was lucky really ... One morning, Jerry played a big raid ... and my mate, a lance corporal, he was laying alongside and he got wounded, seriously wounded, and we went to dress him and pick him up out of the trench. We put him on the parapet, blow me if another shell didn't come over and blew him to pieces. I'd just gone round to see some more mates in the other trench and this other shell came over before we could get him off the stretcher, and blew him to pieces. Oh it was wicked, and all for a franc, ten pence a day! ...'

The memories were so vivid, so real still, after more than 50 years. He remembered how awful the living conditions were, 'the filth'...

'You used to sit on a June or July day in the dug-out in the sunken road there, put the cigarette down the seams of your trousers to burn the lice off, that was the worst part of it, shocking ... I bet vests, pants, trousers and greatcoats were as high as this building to be burnt, to be incinerated, much higher than this room, stacks of uniforms, shirts and pants, vests, socks, all alive, you could see them moving. Oh people don't realize what a filthy job it was, ... that was the worst part, you were in the trenches day and night, stuck in the trench, doing nothing, only walking up and down, especially on a hot blooming day in a bunk hole under the trench. You would dig out a bunk hole so you could get your body in out of the rain... Laugh now, I couldn't then. What was it for? No good at all, was it.'

He could remember the contrast between the experienced soldiers and the young recruits sent out in 1918 who didn't know what they were coming to.

'... absolutely terrible, young chaps come out at 18, didn't understand nothing about it ... when a seasoned man had been there, he knew a bit about it ... the old Boer war sergeant majors and sergeants trained us and they knew what to do ... if you get into trouble, he said, jump into a shell hole, he said, you'll never get one in there, very unfortunate if you do ... get one by the side of it, but never in the same one ... and I learned the dodge of that really...'

He remembered hearing a wounded soldier out in no-man's-land shouting for his mother.

'...it was night-time, a sergeant and two or three of us went out to see if we could find him, poor fellow was hollering "mother, mother" ... We couldn't find him, and old Jerry, he was sending up ground flares, and of course we couldn't move else they'd shoot us down ... we couldn't get the poor fellow, he was laying out there hollering "mother, mother"...'

He had so many vivid memories of the dead, the great numbers waiting for burial.

'Poor fellows, laying there, hundreds of them... up there at the battle of the Vimy ridge, I thought they were troops waiting to go over, you know, to take the trenches, hundreds of them there were ... when we got a bit nearer they were all corpses.'

And unburied ...

'I was walking back on a route march one day and we were going through where a battle had been fought, and we walked through some farmland, and there were four or five officers lying there, Australians, skeletons, they had never found them, you know. It's awful to talk about, but that's how it was ...'

Most horrific of all for him was the thought that he had been part of all the killing.

'Oh it don't do to tell you the things, shocking it was... absolutely cold murder, it was either them or us. You couldn't help yourself. You had to do it, and do your duty ... Who wanted to go out there? I didn't want to go out there and kill anybody. Do you know that in 1918 when Jerry tried to shove us back on the coast, I'd got half a hundredweight of bullets for my machine gun ... then the orders came through to cease fire, make your way and get out of it ... the bullets had burned the barrel of my gun out ... I'd worn the barrel right out with the fire.'

It seemed that it did him some good to unburden himself of these memories by speaking about them to someone else. He could remember it all, he said. He had 'too much memory'. At the same time he realized the value of the historical record he held within him. If only he had been a 'scholar', he said, he could write a 'damned good book'. He had heard that a new book was coming out on the battle of the Somme and was very keen to get hold of it to see what the author said about the battle, 'whether he's written the gospel about it'. But he didn't want to go back to the battlefields. 'No, I might have gone one time, but I don't think I want to go back there now... it's all grown over ... no, I've seen quite enough of it.'

Mr Austin was right to say that he had been lucky to survive but it also seemed remarkable that he had preserved his sensitivity through those four years of war. He had never become indifferent to the experience of suffering he had seen. What struck me in particular was his sympathetic view of the German adversary.

'... I was sorry for the Germans ... we went around the trenches to find the Germans that were dead ... to take their pay books as well as our own boys', and there were fellows there, couldn't have been up the line more than a couple of days, young officers, lovely and smart, they were in the prime of their life. What a waste of life!'

He remembered one German they had taken prisoner.

'... he had the Iron Cross ... and when they lined them up he didn't want it to be found out he'd got one, you see, so he took it off and dropped it on the ground and I didn't say nothing and our sergeant didn't take no notice, good job too, because they would have mobbed him you see.'

And another who expressed his own feelings.

'... our sergeant said to the Jerry sergeant major, "Who's going to win this war, Jerry?" This German could speak better English than I could. He shouted out to our sergeant, "All I know is that those who started this war ought to be where we've been!"... I always remember that ...'

After all, the war had been a terrible experience both for the British and the Germans. They had suffered together.

'What was it for? ... all for no good. We had all that millions of money thrown away and there's people got no houses to live in ain't there. And there's all these slums and they go and throw millions away to kill one another ... It was the same for the Germans.'

He had managed to live with these memories. He could even see the funny side of some things.

'... well I remember the first morning I went out to France, we were out on parade, and we had some observation balloons up to tell us where the German lines were ... blow me that morning old Jerry came over and shot these down ... I thought to myself, "That's a good start" ... you can't help laughing ... terrible things they were.'

Other things seemed funny rather in retrospect.

'... airplanes in those days, they dropped the bombs by hand over the side, trying to find our 18-lb guns. I can picture them now hanging over the side dropping down the big bombs by hand ... you can see the funny side of it now, but you couldn't then.'

Other things had been so strange. The world had taken on an unreal character.

'... it was the time I was up at Ypres, we had to take some rations up for the front line, and we got split up ... I got left on my own ... and I came by the sunken road and some tracks and a little further on there was a big shell hole and a Jerry sitting there ... he had his round pillbox hat on ... I was scared stiff. I didn't know what to do. He might have shot me dead. There might have been two or three more to shoot me. I didn't like to go and speak to him, what a shock, he was sitting there large as life with this pillbox hat on ... I reported it to the officer when I got back to camp and he said we couldn't do anything about it. He might have been dead he said, or shell shocked or something ... but it did seem funny to see him with his hat on and that, sitting there in the shell hole.'

Although Mr Austin spoke mainly to me about the First World War, he was not reticent about expressing his views on contemporary life as well. He expressed the same bewilderment about behaviour that he could not make sense of, such as terrorism and demands for higher and higher pay.

'... I can't get to the bottom of it all, funny world altogether. Gets you beat don't it ... I can't make it out at all ...'

The values of contemporary working men, 'arguing the point', not letting managers run the firm, offended the values he had been brought up with. Excessive pay demands, he was sure, would lead to massive unemployment. For him the simple pleasures of life were best. He greatly enjoyed walking out in the local parks. But now the noise and the pollution caused by traffic bothered him. In this respect the old days certainly had been much better.

From the time I recorded these conversations with him, Mr Austin lived another eight years to the age of 96, and I spoke to him on five occasions in that time. On each occasion he took a personal interest in me, and particularly in my work in Holland. He was really pleased to hear about my marriage. He remained close to and saw a lot of his son.

He was fortunate to remain fit, and he continued to enjoy walking out quite a distance to Bushey and Richmond Park, where he could 'hear the birds and feel at peace'. When I last saw him, aged nearly 94, he was walking out to the park. He said he still felt comfortable, though a bit doddery now. He wished me to live so long. He died a couple of years later in hospital, where he had been taken a few days previously complaining of pain and weakness.

On each of these latter occasions his conversation with me quickly turned again to the war. He still had many stories to tell, and his memories never lost their intensity. 'I wish I had been knocked out earlier,' he said again, 'the sights I've seen!' He expressed the same sense of bewildered surprise to be still alive and the same pity for the Germans as for the British. On the last occasion we met, he told me he had finally got the book on the Somme that he had heard of a few years before. Yes, it had told the truth about how dreadful it had all been. He was glad about that. That was some justice at least.

This sense of 'luck' dominated his whole attitude to his past life. To questioning on his past life he expressed complete satisfaction. How could he complain about anything, when so many others had died young. His reminiscence, as Miss Smith's, had a natural and easy quality to it, although his memories, in contrast to hers, were of unpleasant events. By speaking about them incessantly he seemed to exorcize the hold they had on him, and they did not disturb him beyond measure. But coming to terms with being part of such mass murder would be too much to expect. Indeed, his repeatedly expressed attitude of horror seemed a perfectly sane reaction.

The fact that he had been part of the Great War gave his life a certain significance, and the knowledge that he had coped with such terrible events and survived made the other difficulties he faced insignificant by comparison. He had no ready answers to life's problems. There was a wistful bewilderment in his attitude to his whole life, dominated as it was by memories of the war. 'Yes, I can see the funny part of it, it makes me smile, you wonder how you managed really.'

Mr Cook

Mr Cook was a friendly, cheery man, 77 years old, of large build and with a rosy complexion. He had spent over 50 years working as an engineer on tugs on the River Thames, and life on the water was very much part of him. He described himself as having the 'lungs and heart of a battleship'. There was a lot he wanted to tell me of his career with tugs. The very first story he told me was of the time when he, like Mr Austin, had been part of history, in the evacuation of the British Army from Dunkirk in the Second World War.

'... we had three runs across to Dunkirk ... we started from the 24th May, 1940 up to the 2nd June ... we used to bring them into Dover, then we used to go over in the night time and fetch some more over ...'

He liked to describe the special characteristics of the tugs he had worked on. The one he had used in the relief of Dunkirk was: '...a big ship, a steam tug with big funnels for the draught and the coal, yes a big tug, she used to tow all the big ships in London when it was peace time'. But this particular tug was lost as he ran aground on the last voyage over.

'... I was coming out of Dunkirk with Frenchmen and we got on this wreck ... we stopped there for a little while till the sea laid a bit then we tried to get off. As I worked the engine she stripped the blades of my propeller and broke all the steam steering gear off the tug, made us useless. They had to come and take the Frenchmen off in another boat, and a Belgian fishing boat with bread, which was taking the bread up the firing line into Dunkirk, took us off ...'

That was, he thought, the last he had seen of her.

Mr Cook had followed in the footsteps of his father, who had been a lighterman on the river. He first went on the river in his home town of Kingston-upon-Thames in 1912, when he was 18, stayed there for six years before moving to a bigger firm in the port of London in 1918. He could not join the army in the First World War because of an accident while 'scrumping' for apples when he was 14, which caused one of his legs to shorten. Despite treatment the leg became half an inch shorter than the other and he had to wear special shoes for the rest of his life. Five other brothers had joined up in the war. One was killed and two badly disabled. Another brother, also a tugman, had towed the shells over for the army from Richborough to Calais. Mr Cook had 'done the next best thing' and had helped the war effort with his work on the tugs.

Mr Cook remained with the one company in London for 49 years and had seen it prosper.

'... I was on small tugs to begin with and as we carried on they bought bigger tugs and after that they bought even bigger towing tugs, about 700–800 horse power they were. Then coal got to be dear and repairs were high, so they went in for diesels. Oh yes, we had some lovely big diesel jobs, beautiful tugs they were, absolutely kept spick and span...'

He was very satisfied with the career he had followed, and showed the testimonial he had received from his boss when he left in 1967. He had been fortunate to work with 'decent skippers'. There had been many happy times, even 'times when he didn't want to come home!'. He had left the job a few months short of his 50 years because his wife was seriously ill with cancer. Together they had applied to come and live in a sheltered housing scheme. But his wife had died in the summer of the previous year, just before the place had become available. His son and daughter had encouraged him to move nonetheless, and they were good to him he said—his daughter visiting him usually twice a week—and made sure he was very much part of family events. He also saw quite a lot of friends and old neighbours from the area from which he had just moved into sheltered housing. He also continued to go to the workingmen's club as he had done for many years and enjoyed the company there. He also liked gardening, and had done a lot of planting of roses and other flowers in beds around the housing complex.

In the year I first got to know him, although coping well and expressing positive attitudes to his situation, it was clear that he was still very much grieving for his wife. He said that he 'was always thinking about her'. And despite his happy memories there was also 'a lot of things' in his life which he said he wished he had not done, memories which made him feel badly about himself.

He also had other difficulties. Arthritis was now increasing in his hips and knees and made it difficult for him to move around. Most upsettingly too, his old tug company had suspended his small pension payments for the last twelve months. The docks were shutting, his old company had very little work, and the original owner's family was no longer in charge. They had amalgamated with another firm. It had not been a compulsory pension, but a payment of £32 a quarter in recognition of his long years of service. He felt the change of attitude badly. He would like to say to his old boss 'that's not the way you have always been to us!'. The firm they had gone in with was known for being 'mean'. He remembered how they used to make their men keep on with their scrubbing brushes until they were absolutely worn out!

Despite the areas of regret in his life, reminiscing he said was a great help to him in getting over difficulties. He had a lot of good stories to tell me. Unlike Miss Smith, who was concerned to tell me how good things had been in the old days, and Mr Austin who wanted to tell me his enduring impressions of war, Mr Cook's reminiscences focussed on his own achievements.

Once he had rescued a woman who had thrown herself off Tower Bridge. It had been the start of his problems with his leg.

'...we had a tug there at Tower Bridge to pull the ships through and we used to go and pick them up... well this Saturday morning this old dear threw herself off Tower Bridge and I saw her come down and she came floating up alongside, and the tide was coming up fast and I got hold of her, went over the side ... and I held her—my knee against the tug until help came—a man came from a little ship that was moored up. He jumped in and we got her aboard this little ship. We couldn't get her aboard the tug, she was 16 stone ... we towed this ship up to Tower Pier, and by the time we got up there, there was an ambulance waiting for her. Well the son came down in the evening to thank our skipper for what he done and all that. He told him that she'd tried to commit suicide, she'd just come out of a mental hospital ... but that was the start of this leg, oh yes, that was the start of this knee. Things that I've done, injuries that I've done in helping somebody else!'

He had also appeared in films.

'... they used to pick us out to take pictures ... there was one picture where they wanted an extra so they got the engineer up, old Tom McDonald, and it was a bit of a rough and tumble picture, and they hit a bloke that they thought was the right one, instead of that they hit this McDonald and knocked his damned teeth out. He had false teeth, and they knocked them right out, oh it was a laugh. Then the bloke who had to pull the lever in the engine room couldn't pull it up, and I had to go down, turn the engine over and reverse it, see. The engine room was filled up with steam ... I had to get all his gear on, get a beard round me. I got £14 for that ... then I had £7 just for going on board a barge as they were making her fast onto another barge ...'

Work during the Second World War was a source of a lot of reminiscences too.

'... it was much hotter in the docks in London than what it was getting to Dunkirk and back. We had terrible nights in the old dock. We had to tow all the ships out who were up in the river because they used to drop the bombs up on the dock gates, and they were frightened all the water would come out the dock, see. The ships would be laying on their side.'

'... the tanker was set ablaze by one of these mines. We was one of the tugs towing her. Put her ashore, alongside a wharf, the seas were practically alight. Oh yes, you youngsters don't know ... we fought for freedom for you chaps to live.'

But above all he reminisced of happy times. He had felt at home in his job and could take some liberties with his employers. 'The guvnor said I was the sauciest engineer in the job!'

He liked to show me the photos he had of the different tugs he had worked on.

'... that's one of our diesel jobs, smashing job, she was beautiful, 750 horse power and she could put another 50 horse power on her. Lovely tug she was. She was a big boat, oh she was a beautiful boat, her pistons were tight, she used to tow barges up to Tilbury Dock for two hours and about 1200 ton ...'

He had worked hard.

'We used to work 36 hours right off. From six o'clock Monday morning we'd work right up till about six o'clock Tuesday night ... or if you were fog bound you'd do your week's work 48 hours right off in the fog, then you'd come on again like the end of the week and do some more overtime when the fog cleared. See we were so busy, all the work got hung up in London. See, if all the stuff on the wharf got hung up, then you had to work overtime. Of course we didn't mind that because then we got extra money for it and in them days you were glad to get it, not like they are these days, making £40 for leaning on a shovel!'

Mr Cook reiterated many times the thought that he had been part of a hard working generation. Standards had deteriorated badly. His feelings were very understandable considering he had been part of the dock industry whose severe decline epitomized the decline of British trading activity since the war. The papermills he spoke of down the estuary of the Thames, where he had towed barges full of wood pulp from Canada, were gone. They could now make the paper themselves in Canada. There was very little activity indeed at the present day in the London docks. The world was a different place, he said, not suited for older people!

'... don't matter where you go, it's different. Even the kind of people are different. The youngsters, you go to get on the bus and they'll shove you off and get on ... to my idea everything's changed ... years ago we couldn't say that we weren't going to do a job ... if they sack anyone now they come out on strike ... we had to work for our money. Nowadays they go and get this money for nothing. They won't work all the time they can get the money. That money ought to be for us that's done work, and worked for it—for us old age pensioners. We've got a job to live!'

I got to know Mr Cook well in the years that followed and visited him on eleven occasions over 14 years. When I last saw him in the summer of 1985, he was in good spirits. His appearance was remarkably similar to 14 years before. His arthritis, however, had got much worse, in his shoulders and neck as well as hip and knees, and for more than five years he had only been able to walk with sticks. The arthritis gave him a lot of pain from time to time. He had the assistance of a home help once a week. Nevertheless his lifestyle was not very different. He saw his daughter two or three times a week and his son once a week. He also saw a lot of old friends. His daughter took him out shopping every week, and he took a great pleasure in sitting out in the gardens of the housing complex which he had planted himself. For Christmas 1984 he had got the gardener to help him put up coloured lights and balloons in his own room. He joined in actively in the various social gatherings the new warden organised.

To the questions I asked him on morale in 1981 he answered even more positively than ten years previously. Then he had been greatly under the impact of losing his wife. But now he was very cheerful indeed. He did a lot of the housework himself and was proud of it. He did not feel ill. He had plenty of interests—he'd always enjoyed doing the cooking, even when his wife was alive. He had 'got his share of happiness'. The source of his success, he thought, was his 'willpower'. It was no good letting oneself 'go down in the dumps'. He was not afraid of death. He believed in God but not, so it seemed, in an afterlife.

He felt lucky and was generally satisfied with his life. There were some things he would change, but there were no thoughts that disturbed him as they had done following his wife's death. His attitude to reminiscing had become if anything, more positive. He said he could remember things well and greatly enjoyed thinking about the past. He said he even dreamed about tugs! He continued to tell me stories about life on the river. He would say often that he had 'a lot to tell me'.

Mr Cook lived long enough to feel the impact of a growth of interest in the Second World War and in oral history generally. When I last saw him he showed me a coloured photograph he had just received of the very tug he thought he would never see again, stranded on the beach at Dunkirk in 1940 along with many military vehicles. The photograph had been taken at the time by an American photographer and a copy had now been sent to him by the latest successor to his old tug firm, now no longer based in London but in Felixstowe. Someone was coming to see him soon to interview him about his experiences at that time. The tug company was at last prospering again in its new base and was sending his pension regularly again, along with letters which kept him up to date with developments. It was as he deserved after his long years of service.

He maintained his negative opinion on the state of the world. In fact he was even more convinced that things were getting worse, with increasing unemployment and dangers of war. When I saw him soon after the Falklands war in 1982 he was quite clear in his judgement that 'it was not worth' the loss of life involved. The year before I was with him when an old friend called, the son of his former neighbours. His parents were both dead and he said to me how glad he was to be able to come and talk with Mr Cook about old times. They talked a lot about happy memories, of Kingston in the past—cricket on the green 'with a jug of beer', 'glorious food' that could be bought so cheap in the evenings, the countryside around with goats and blackberrying in September, a lively market in town to which people brought their own produce. It had still been 'old England' even up to the 1950s. The passing of the seasons then had been magical. People made their own enjoyments, they cared about one another. They were poorer, but happier. Now it was nothing but 'rushing, noise and violence'. Young people no longer had respect for authority. When he came to Mr Cook, he said, he could be at peace, forget his present worries and go back in memories to this happier time. This was a tribute indeed. Mr Cook was a refuge, a source of solace. He stood for an older, better time.

Reminiscing then was a very real role for Mr Cook—something which he both valued and for which he was valued. He agreed strongly that memories of the past helped him to cope with the difficulties of old age. His life appeared on the face of it—although he kept some parts hidden—to have been relatively un-problematic. He had followed the same career as his father, had greatly enjoyed it and kept it up for as long as possible. But there had been difficulties and dis-appointments, starting with his accident as a boy. He had had to work hard through two world wars, for little pay and little pension. Still his life had been happy and eventful, and he had done this job well. Now he could use the past to confirm the image that he had of himself as a capable, self sufficient person and to keep others informed and entertained. He seemed to be a good example of the 'story telling' reminiscer described by McMahon and Rhudick (1964) and to exemplify the positive relationship found between reminiscing and adjustment that is described in some studies (for example Havighurst and Glasser, 1972).

It would though be misleading to attribute exclusive importance to Mr Cook's reminiscing in explaining his 'successful ageing'. Other strengths he possessed were close family contacts and his ability to look after himself which he had developed in earlier life. Perhaps most significant of all was his strong belief in his own powers, but as already said this too was based on his own successful career. Last but not least he had a very noticeable sense of humour. When I last said goodbye to him he reminded me next time to park in the official car park. 'Tell them you're Mr Cook's solicitor coming to pay him out £10,000!'

Subsequent History of Other Cases

Miss Smith, Mr Austin and Mr Cook all appeared to cope well with the buffets of old age, and declining physical powers in particular. From the evidence collected it is plausible to suggest that a positive view of their past lives and their memories and active involvement in reminiscing played some part in their successful ageing, in maintaining a strong sense of identity based in the present but firmly anchored in the past. How far was this true of the other people in the same group who in 1970–71 expressed the same positive, valuing attitude to their memories?

The evidence on the adaptive value of such an orientation certainly appears quite strong from a consideration of the material I collected about them. Al-together nine people lived another six years or more and appeared to maintain reasonably high morale as well as a positive attitude to reminiscing. Mrs Manners and Mrs Parsons, both to be discussed in Chapter 9, coped remarkably well with problems of ill health that dogged them in their remaining years. Both were fine examples of positive thinking about life in general. Mrs Manners' serene acceptance of her health difficulties aroused great admiration in all who knew her. Mrs Parsons in contrast did not accept passively the help that was offered from the health services, and probably made life quite difficult for those who tried to help her. But she also seems to have aroused equal admiration in those who knew her. Both had rich interior lives in which reminiscence played a natural part, as a source of happy memories and of lessons for the present.

Miss Arnold lived another eight years to the age of 86 and I saw her on two occasions in this time. Her arthritis too increasingly incapacitated her, but she maintained a reasonably high morale. She disliked the housing complex where she lived and wished she had not left her own home. But the past remained an important source of satisfaction to her. Her memories of a good family life and her continued contacts with her brother and her nephew were essential to her. She followed closely her nephew's career. Mrs Black managed to secure a move seven years later to another sheltered housing scheme in order to be nearer friends and relatives and lived happily there for a further two years.

Mr Locke's life was a remarkable story of successful ageing. Despite his blindness he continued to maintain his own household and to go every year on his holiday to Austria. He preferred to live dangerously and eventually died of heart failure after a fall down the stairs nine years later at the age of 80. Right up to the end he played a leading part in the social life of the sheltered housing scheme where he lived and was much admired. He reminisced to a moderate degree and liked telling stories with a humourous ending. He laughed particularly at the attitudes of the 'grumblers' among his neighbours.

Of particular interest was the further history of Mrs Somerton who when I first met her was still depressed following her husband's death. She seemed to resolve her problems in a few years and ten years later, when I saw her (before her last illness) she had reasonably high morale. Given her advanced age (88 years) and physical complaints that had made her housebound for more than ten years, this change of mood is quite noteworthy. In retrospect it seems significant that even in her depressed state ten years earlier she had described her memories as being of great value to her and did not say that they made her more depressed. They continued to be very important to her and she was fortunate to have regular visits from her brother with whom she said she reminisced a lot.

Of those who lived a shorter time, the evidence I collected both from themselves and others who knew them suggested that eight of the remaining twelve maintained high morale until their deaths. Mr Turner kept on gardening until the end. When I visited him in his last year he again emphasized the importance of 'guts' and 'not giving in'. Both he and Mr Dennis had a lot more stories to tell me. When I last met Miss Jansen she was quietly contented and as considerate as ever. She apologized repeatedly for not being a good conversationalist. But her past life gave her a lot of satisfaction. She repeated the story of how she had left Denmark as a young woman to come to England in order to become a nanny. Her room was the complete contrast to the austere room of Mrs Parsons (see Chapter 9), for example. It was prettily decorated with embroidery and she had many photographs around of all the children she had looked after in her life. When I visited Mr Cohen at 90 he expressed himself well satisfied with his life. His mistakes in business that he had commented on a couple of years before seemed even less important to him now. Money, he said, was not the important thing in life, as long as one had enough. He felt well and he had 'three good sons', with one of whom he was going to stay for the Jewish New Year.

There were four people in the group, however, who remained or became depressed. Mr Pym and Mr Laver, already in very poor physical health when I first met them, died in the following year before I could see them again. Miss Trickett who was losing her sight and who was disturbed by her memory deterioration, struggled on a little while. But she very much regretted the move away from her old neighbourhood, her church and friends, and was greatly disturbed by what she saw as changed behaviour in society. Although she said that reminiscence was important to her it did not help her very much. The next year she went into an old people's home and died the year after. Mrs Edwards' memory deteriorated too at a rapid rate, and she became depressed. Her hopes of an active and enjoyable old age which she had expressed only two years previously had been destroyed. She died the next year. Both Miss Trickett and Mrs Edwards had to experience the devastating impact of mental decline virtually unsupported.

Nevertheless, if one discounts these few cases in all of which people experienced severe disability with rapid onset, a positive attitude to reminiscence did appear to be associated with some degree of resilience to loss. The evidence from this study would suggest that happy reminiscence of the nature that has been described should be regarded as a positive prognostic factor in old age, to be encouraged rather than discouraged.

Chapter 6

Regret and Resolution

Distinguishing Characteristics

In their discussion of Erikson's and Butler's writings on the achievement of integrity and life review processes in later life, Lieberman and Tobin, as already described in Chapter 2, argue that it is unrealistic to assume that all or even most human beings have the necessary inner skills and/or supportive context to achieve a thorough going and conscientious review (Lieberman and Tobin, 1983). Their own research suggests how often people use their personal past to construct 'mythical' images. Memory is used selectively. Key events are dramatized, others dismissed. The result is a picture of the self that is acceptable both to the individual and to others. It serves to maintain a sense of stability in the present.

And yet it is a precarious thing, this acceptance, which we try to win from others and from ourselves, with so much care. The more there is to be hidden the more effort is required. We cannot or dare not detach ourselves completely from reality. Our self concept has to be built on something solid. Sometimes nagging doubts enter in, and force open the door. We may then see a view of ourselves that is unacceptable. Eight people in this study clearly presented themselves in this way—to varying degrees, but still noticeably. They felt their lives not only to have been unsatisfactory but to have been unworthy and unacceptable. There was no 'story' or 'myth' they could construct which could more than in part dignify the account of their life history.

Significantly perhaps they were a younger group than the rest of the sample, with no-one older than 78. Mr Bennett had married late in life and 'made a bad mistake' in doing so. He and his wife had quarrelled a lot over the upbringing of their children. He had 'belted' a daughter who had become promiscuous, for which he had been taken to court, and his wife had later separated from him on grounds of mental cruelty. It 'drove him mad' to think back on this period, but he could not help it. Mrs Jones had married at 16. Her first five children had died early in life because she 'did not know how to look after them'. She said she often pondered now whether she could have saved them. Her relationships with her surviving children were strained. She had quarrelled a lot with them and regretted this. She was, she said, her 'own worst enemy'. She was in much discomfort from a twisted gut, and she wanted to die. Mr Elton had served a prison sentence for theft at the end of the Second World War. He had 'had to do' it to support his wife and family. He still greatly resented that whole episode in his life. It had humiliated him in particular that he had not been able to obtain a free health service after he came out because of his prison record. His friends had not looked after his wife, as they had promised him, when he was in prison, and she had had a very difficult time and died soon after his release. He was 'always thinking about her'. He 'argued with himself' over what had happened and what he had done. He just sat and thought, and he said that some of his thoughts were 'terrible'.

Not all had such tragic stories to tell, but even apparently happy lives can seem empty and meaningless in retrospect. Mr Thompson had enjoyed himself a good deal in life. In the First World War he had been lucky enough to travel a lot in Egypt and Palestine, countries he had found full of interest. After the war he had spent some time in America, around the period of prohibition. His life though had gradually come to revolve around gambling. He had been in the famous casinos of the South of France. He had eventually set up his own betting shop in the centre of London, but now he complained greatly of loneliness and felt he had been unlucky with his family. His health was poor (he had severe emphysema) and he could move around only a little. His children were pressing him to move into an old people's home. Reminiscence, he said, brought him little solace, only a sense of 'wasted chances'. Gambling had been his prime love. He had 'wanted to be a millionaire'. But he had been a 'silly mug'. Money was 'no good to you'. He felt very lonely, with no-one to talk to. He was the only man within the sheltered housing scheme and he said he disliked older women's company.

Also Mr Gatting had had his good days. He had had various adventures, always been out and about, indulged for a time in smuggling until his wife stopped him, and even fought with gangsters. He was proud of his 'crafty' nature, bred, he said, out of a poor childhood where he had had to learn to 'scrounge' and his 'ready wit'. He had not let people get the better of him. He liked to quote the Frank Sinatra song, 'I did it my way'. But now alone and dis-abled after a fall, life seemed so 'boring' to him. He felt he was just waiting for the end. What was the point of it all, 'just cooking and washing up, cooking and washing up'. Thoughts of the past often came before his mind, and disturbed him. Reminiscing, he said, definitely did not give him a good feeling or give him a sense of appreciation of his life. Rather when he came to 'certain items' he had to say to himself 'forget it'. He would not enlarge further on these comments.

The eight people in the study who were disturbed by their regrets included some who without doubt needed some form of intervention to help them resolve their problems. Mr Bennett in particular could find no way out of his negative thinking which obsessed and persecuted him. Mrs Jones also was deeply depressed about the conflict with her family—and her sad feelings were fed by accusatory thoughts about the children she had lost when she was young. Mr Elton by contrast fought his thoughts, defended his past actions, and spoke in an aggressive way about many matters, including young people and 'toffee nosed foreign Jews' in the housing complex in which he lived. But all eight described themselves as 'lonely' and were more or less discontented with their own company and their own thoughts.

The five people already described all died within a short period of time—less than two years. The three people who are the subject of the following case studies all lived a much longer time, and this should be borne in mind in drawing any generalizations from their cases. None of the three probably had as severe problems with troubling feelings of guilt as some of those already mentioned. There were, however, definite aspects about their past lives which troubled them.

Mr Menash and Mr Currie were similar in some respects. Despite their dissatisfaction with their past lives, they liked to talk about them with me. They did not shy away from addressing the areas that caused them pain, as a number of other people I met did. In fact they exemplified the relationship referred to in Chapter 4 between dissatisfaction with past life, active life review and a reasonably high morale, in contrast to the low morale of those who avoided speaking about an unsatisfactory past. They were similar too in that both had regrets about failures in their working life, and about their inability to marry which they attributed to financial difficulties in the period of economic slump in the late 1920s and early 1930s.

Miss Martin's case is quite different in that her life had been sad for reasons she saw as largely beyond her control. But like the others she could not avoid thinking about her past and it was a source of great sorrow and even of despair. She said with conviction that she wished she had not lived. Her living circumstances were depressing in the extreme and it seemed unlikely that she could achieve a greater measure of acceptance of her life.

Mr Menash

When I first met Mr Menash he was 72 years old and had been living in sheltered housing for two years. He had moved there after his doctor diagnosed him to be suffering from angina of the heart and advised retirement. A well educated Armenian, born and brought up in Istanbul, he was always most courteous to me as well as to other people I observed him with. He entertained me with style, usually offering a Martini and savoury snacks. Pleased to talk about contemporary society as well as his past career, he was highly articulate and sometimes rather insistent on his own point of view. His replies on the 16PF personality questionnaire which he agreed to fill in indicated the sensitive side of his character. He had the maximum score on the dimension 'affected by feelings, easily upset'. He also scored very highly on 'undisciplined self conflict'.

He had experienced much upheaval in his early adult life. He had served as a lieutenant in the Turkish army in the First World War, but with the persecution of the Armenian community in the aftermath of the Turkish defeat and the establishment of the regime of Kemal Atatürk, he had looked for a new life. His only sister had married an Armenian Englishman and gone to live in England before the war, and he therefore decided to follow her. Initially he had great success in London in the 1920s building up a trading business, but his career was to continue to be one of ups and downs, of setbacks as well as achievements.

In his accounts of his life there was a strong element of pride both in his achievements and in his resilience in overcoming difficulties. He made disastrous mistakes in the slump of 1929 to 1931 and was almost reduced to bankruptcy by giving too much credit, especially to the overseas firms he was exporting to:

'... I was too ambitious to make money quick and I was giving credit and selling more than I should do, and then the slump came and one after another their bills were coming back "not paid". When I wanted to know why they said, "We are bankrupt, we can't help you". So I lost all that money, in six months I lost £3,700 ... I realized there was some difficulty but by the time I realized this I was in too deep ... I kept carrying on and because of my good name in the trade I got credit from the importers here so that I could carry on. I paid every penny that I did have, that's why I still have the good name today. The merchants that are in the City still respect me because they didn't lose a penny out of me, although I lost nearly all my money. I paid them every bit of my capital ... Today they say to me, "if you come back to the trade we will give you the same credit as before".'

He built up his trade again dealing in Chinese and Turkish carpets, financed by a company in Manchester with which he had family connections. He was entrusted with the sole responsibility for ordering and selling.

'... I designed the Chinese carpets myself, sitting in the office, making the colour scheme, the weight of the carpet, the height of the pile and so on. Then I used to send an order to China to the manufacturer ... The company (in Manchester) would send a letter of credit because Chinese men, they won't take your order unless you give the actual credit to your bank ... I used to get half the profit, they used to get half the profit. If it was a loss, again I was responsible for half the loss just the same. They were very kind to me ... The director used to say, "We will trust you and will do whatever you say".'

But again his success was not to last. With the outbreak of the Second World War trading with China and Turkey ceased. Mr Menash closed his office and went to work in an aircraft factory. As the war came to an end he tried to start up again, but the new Chinese communist government forced drastic price rises on exporters.

'... Instead of £5,000 we would have to put down £25,000 to £35,000. But I didn't want to be responsible for that, it was too big an item for me to be responsible for ... I stopped. I said, "No, I don't want to carry on any more," and I started buying and selling on the market here. Instead of importing and manufacturing myself, I started on the market with the capital that I'd made. I was making a small percentage and I was doing fairly well that way, until I became ill and I had my heart trouble and the doctor said, "You can't do any more, you'll have to retire," and so I stopped.'

Despite the noticeable pride in his accomplishments he was also oppressed by a sense of his own misfortune both in the past and present. Because of his heart condition he walked deliberately very slowly and kept to a strict diet. Even so, he said, doctors had told him he would 'die of a heart attack within two or three years'. Above all he missed his old work setting and acquaintances, and tried to maintain contact.

'... Still now and then I make myself an excuse to go to the City and I start early. I can get a number 8 from here which takes me straight to Liverpool Street ... It takes an hour but still I don't mind. Then I get down to the coffee house [which he used to frequent] and they all come in. There are some younger ones now come into the trade. They still know me through their fathers and so on ... They like to know how life is with me and I like to find out how things are. Some of them are over 70, still carrying on with their business. They never retire in my trade, they work until they die. I'm the only one that did retire through my heart, otherwise I would have carried on ...'

Sometimes he gave advice to the younger men, especially to those who like him were 'without fathers'.

'... I tell them to be careful. Don't get caught by crooks who come round and buy on credit and then they don't pay you. Don't put your eggs all in one basket ... don't give any more at first than £500 credit to any of those (continental exporters), then if they are punctual to pay their bills in time increase it ... but still make sure to find their records, their references and find out what sort of firm they are ... They listen to me ... Experiences should not be very costly. You should get the benefit from men that have already dearly paid for such experiences, and don't do the same mistakes as I did, because I had no advisors, I had no father or anybody else to turn to ...'

His over-all verdict on his life seemed more negative than positive. He had had to work hard for everything he possessed, and as a consequence had not been able to enjoy his life fully. If he were to live his life over again he would not enter so risky a trade. He had lacked guidance, had 'no father to advise' him. Above all he regretted that he had not been able to marry because of financial difficulties. He had 'lost his young days in struggle'. Reminiscing did give him some pleasure but above all a strong sense of regret.

Mr Menash admitted to getting depressed at times but he fought hard to overcome it. He went to meetings of the local Conservative club, also to the local cricket and bowls grounds where he was welcomed as a spectator. He saw quite a lot of his sister's children (she had died soon after the Second World War) and attended sometimes the services at the Armenian Orthodox church in London. He believed in the importance of religion as a disciplining force in this world, although he could not believe in an afterlife. His flat was comfortably furnished, and he had developed a hobby of painting—principally flowers—and examples of his work were displayed around his room.

The values of his own world, however, he saw as greatly under threat. His attitude to present day society was extremely negative. There had been a loss of proper standards of behaviour, parents giving insufficient attention to their children, an increase in violent crime, and workers seeming intent on 'cutting off the branch they are sitting on' by inflationary wage demands coupled with time wasting. They overturned what was for him a principal value in life that 'work and what one produces gives one a good name'.

Sometimes an intolerant note crept into what he said, and even despite his general courtesy a hint of anger and resentment directed to me as a student.

'...You see you people are still not satisfied, you want more money. You get cheap fears and get more money that you need and everything else, and still ...'

Mr Menash lived a further twelve years and his attitudes to both past and present remained constant throughout. When I visited him he entertained me as before. He liked especially to talk of current affairs, the benefits and disadvantages of the common market, the government's attempt to control the trade unions, the problems of Rhodesia and so on. His life followed the same pattern. He remained preoccupied with what he regarded as his imminent death. 'Did you expect to find me alive?' he asked me on one occasion, when I had not visited for some time. He was interested to hear about my career, and pleased that I had married. Marriage was 'the best condition in life'.

His health remained relatively stable for about nine years, but then pain and difficulties in breathing led to the discovery of malignant lung cancer. When I saw him a few months later he said doctors had given him only three to six months to live. Nevertheless he still made his usual efforts to entertain me and to converse about the news of the day. He was also interested in the photographs I showed him of my son. He said that he was glad that I had bought a house, which he had never been able to do.

In the following two years he became very depressed. Pain in the back was a constant problem and he had to go into hospital every three months to have the fluid drained off his lung. He could no longer walk out. He would be glad to die, he said. His eyes had deteriorated so he could not paint anymore, and he was particularly concerned about deterioration in his memory.

In 1981 and 1982 I spoke to him on five occasions and asked him the same questions I had ten years previously. The worst problem he said was loneliness. Although he saw his niece every week and his nephew every month, he felt that they did not give him the support he needed. A lot of the people in the housing complex with whom he used to speak had died and been replaced by people with whom he had nothing in common. The one lady he did still visit had now offended him and hurt his pride when she told him to go away on the last occasion he visited. (I spoke to this lady at the same time and she was puzzled and did not understand why he did not come to her anymore.) Although a lifelong Conservative supporter, he was very critical of the new Thatcher government both for its economic and foreign policy. It was 'provoking' rather than lessening international tension, and following the United States too closely. He was pessimistic about the prospects for nuclear war. Europe would be devastated. He was glad he would not live to see it.

In this period he appeared close to despair and there seemed no possible resolution of his regrets about the past. Rather they were intensified. Throughout these last years he showed in may ways that he still felt that he had been unlucky in life and would change it if he had to live his life over again. His main regret concerned the fact that he had not married. This was strongly associated with his present loneliness. Of his career, he said that he had 'ideals' when he was young, but had not reached his goal, and therefore 'could not feel fulfilled' when old. He said he thought a lot about his twenties when his life was very happy, 'before his misfortunes began'. Most remarkably, too, thoughts about his earlier life in Istanbul came back to him. Previously he had never thought about going back to Turkey but now he would like to be back. He would feel more at home in the surroundings there, he said, even though he realized that the quality of life had probably deteriorated just as much in Turkey as it had in England. Old people had been loved and respected more in the past.

When I last saw him, a year later, a few months before he died, he was very weak, but there had been a significant improvement in his mood. (His doctor in fact had at least treated him for depression with anti-depressant drugs.) He said that he had 'got to put up with his condition'. He did not complain about his family anymore, he no longer thought about being back in Istanbul. Quite the contrary in fact, as he remembered only too well the Turks' cruelty to the Armenians. Nor did he worry about his memory as before, indeed he thought his mental faculties were very good for his age. He saw his friend in the housing scheme regularly again, although not every day, as he was 'less interested in seeing people now'. He hoped to improve a little so that he could go and sit outside in the warmer weather. He was not afraid of death, although he did not believe in an afterlife.

What struck me most, however, was how his attitude to contemporary society had seemed to change. He thought carefully before he responded to my question on the subject and then said it was 'not so bad'. There were certainly 'more opportunities for younger people nowadays'. As for old people, he was not so sure that things were better. But then it was difficult to know what life really had been like for old people in the past. At the end, therefore, his attitudes that had seemed so firm began to dissolve, and he appeared to come to a greater acceptance of his own situation and that of the world in general.

Mr Currie

Mr Currie also expressed a sense of lack of real satisfaction with his achievements in life when I first met him. Like Mr Menash he had felt unable to marry because of the precarious financial position of his life in the 1920s and 1930s, and he said he regretted it now. However, he had as well more troubling thoughts about past relationships with his father and one of his sisters, and these preyed on his mind a lot.

He was born in Newcastle on Tyne in 1896, into a family with two elder sisters. His father was an engineer and moved his family a number of times in search of work. When Mr Currie was little they moved to his father's home area of Portland in Dorset. His father worked on torpedos in the naval base there. Later he took the family to Swindon where he set up a garage in partnership with his brother. At the age of 16 Mr Currie was apprenticed to his father, but 'could not get on with him'. They were 'always pulling apart'. His father remained a source of ambivalent feelings, and Mr Currie spoke to me a lot about him.

On the one hand he had considerable admiration for his father:

'He was very clever really. If only I had half the brains he had I wouldn't be where I am today. He was very clever, clean living, never smoked, never swore . . . He was a Sunday School teacher in the time when he met mother. A clean living man, honest—in fact he put too much in his work to make it pay. That's why he didn't succeed in business. He wasn't a business man. I can give you an instance. A man came in and said he wanted some brakes fitted on his bike and he wanted it done in a hurry. My father turned round and said to him, "Your life depends on these brakes. If you don't permit me to take my time and do it as I want to do it, you had better take the job somewhere else". He was a man like that, conscientious. He turned everything out to perfection.'

His father was an active trade unionist as well who 'did a lot of work behind the scenes', a man of high standards who left a lasting influence even on his son's speech:

'. . . when we were round the table or anything and we spoke ungrammatically, then he would check us immediately, and if we'd gone through a sentence at the table he would make us go right through it from the beginning. And I often find myself doing it now, if I'm making a sentence . . . I go right back to the commencement . . .'

But there were also important aspects of his father that he found hard to accept.

'Yes he was a good living man but he was, shall I say, he should never have been married . . . He wasn't the marrying type, he was wrapped up in his work.'

He was also harsh. He gave his son a number of beatings and there was one incident in particular that stuck in his mind.

'. . . I was about 13 going on for 14 . . . When we used to finish school and it used to rain we played in this shed of my father's, us kids used to go in out of the rain and play in it . . . One night a sister of one of these kids came up for him, wanted to know where he was because it was raining and she took him back home. Apparently he told her a yarn, that I had pulled his pants down, and she came up and complained to my father about it. He didn't go into any details, he just got hold of me and gave me a belting . . . In those days motor cycles were driven by belts, composition of rubber and leather, and I got the life beaten out of me, I was screaming . . . He didn't ask, he just took the other person's story and got cracking on me . . . I could stand a bit of punishment, but he left weals on me.'

He 'never forgave' his father for this beating and he was to remind his father about it many years later when his father was old.

'It was the last thing that I spoke to my father about. We were on kind of friendly terms and I used to go and see him occasionally . . . And one day it cropped up about this occasion. Something happened and I cracked . . . I thought, "I'm never going to let you get away with it". And I said to him, "I'll never forgive you for that beating that you gave me" ... He said he didn't remember. He didn't want to remember, and said "if you don't like it you need not come back to see me again". The next time I saw him he was in his coffin.'

As a boy apprenticed to his father Mr Currie found himself in an impasse. 'I kept leaving him and he kept sacking me.' It was his sister who suggested a way out. She was already a tailoress and encouraged him to take up the same trade. He was pleased at the idea. 'I thought I'll be able to make my own suits ... I was a man about town.' But he missed engineering.

'I would like to have gone on with engineering. The mistake was my father apprenticed me under him. I couldn't get on with him. If he had apprenticed me with another engineering concern I would have made good, because even though I say it myself I have an inventive mind. I can improvise things, I'm handy with tools, and had I had the right tuition I'm sure I could have made good and been more pleased with myself. I could have achieved something.'

Tailoring was too sedentary an occupation for him and he did not enjoy the work.

But it was not long before his life was altered by the First World War. He volunteered for service in 1914 and after a number of false starts found himself in India. It was there that he first learned the pleasure of travelling and indeed the war years were happy years for him stationed in the hills on the Northern Frontier. He had preserved many photographs and mementoes from this time.

He was not to return to England until 1919, by which time his mother had died. He was 23 and still not an established tailor. He found work in Bath but it was poorly paid. In 1926 his other sister, who had married and emigrated for some years to America, encouraged him to follow. But work was no easier to find there. He felt discrimination against him as an Englishman and only by the help of another Swindon man was he able to find a job, working the lifts at GEC in New York. With the crash of 1929 and people being thrown out of work all around him, he saw any prospects he might have disappearing, and he used the spare cash he still had to come back to England. Thereafter he worked at a number of jobs, including Spitfire construction during the Second World War, hospital portering and working the lifts again, this time in a large department store. Back trouble led him to retire at 69 and thereafter he moved to the sheltered housing scheme where I met him.

He was not happy about the course his life had followed.

'As I have been getting older I often think to myself had I buckled down could I have made a better man of myself as regards education and business? My father was clever, my sister was very clever ... I was the dullest of the crowd. Whether it was because I was more interested in playing than I was in working, it may have been that, but I couldn't concentrate ... I could never concentrate with my learning at school. My ideas were as soon as I came out of school to get a tennis ball and go up some side alley and pick a team and have a game of football ... but you see I never made anything of that, I could have concentrated and become a professional footballer...'

Another important area of regret in his life was his failure to marry. Indeed the period of life which he said he thought the most back on was the 1920s, after he came back from India and was living in Bath. He had a number of girlfriends and in particular there was one married woman with whom he was very much in love. His younger sister was scandalized, but he said it was his low pay which really prevented him from marrying. 'In those days you had to be able to keep a woman ... How was I able to marry on 25 shillings a week?' Having to leave her hurt him very much. It was part of the reason he went to America.

Also in later life there were particular regrets.

'... when you have hurt those that you sort of love it hits you hard. Things you know like I remember once my younger sister was a district nurse down at Brighton. I used to go down to visit her at weekends. Well she never married. I used to go on thinking well we're two left and it would be nice if later on we could get a house to ourselves, buy a house. And I did suggest it. But I'm afraid I never made any movement and it was brought back to me you know and I took offence and I took my bag and baggage and got out.'

His other sister he had not seen since 1945 when his younger sister died. She had refused to come to the funeral and Mr Currie had told her then that he would not see her again. He did not know whether she was alive or dead. Like his father he had not been good at forgiving.

Mr Currie seemed to greatly appreciate the opportunity I gave him to talk over things. He appeared already to be engaged in a process of life review.

'There's heaps of things that I would alter if I had my time over again ... things which I often think about ... I suppose it's being on long journeys, things go through your mind, whereas before I've always been so busy, meeting people and enjoying myself and getting the most out of life instead of thinking of the wrongs that I've done. It comes to me now lots of things that I wouldn't do again if I had my way again, causing hurt to people ...'

There was a lot too about his present life that he found it difficult to come to terms with. He missed his old activities and contacts. Friends were 'hard to come by'. He felt rejected and this made him angry. These feelings merged with the genuine distress he also experienced at the decline of the country's fortunes and in the old standards of behaviour.

'To think of this country, what we've been through and fought and what we're thought of now. I know people that walk past me in the street now. I can keep a stiff upper lip thank God—let 'em walk—but those people I've done favours for. I worked in a hospital for 15 years. I used to do favours for the sisters and nurses and various other people that it wasn't necessary for me to do, but I did them out of the kindness of my heart ... I see them in Kingston market and they don't want to know you now. You're old, they don't want to know. But going back to the country, when you come to think of what we've given. I gave five years of the best of my life ... what annoys me is that all we fought for, these kids of today are throwing away. All they are out for is a good time without working for it ...'

Sometimes he was angry with me, before I gained his confidence, and often as he spoke about the country he was close to tears. In his general sensitivity, his regrets about his past life and his negative attitudes to modern society he had close similarities with Mr Menash.

Unlike Mr Menash though he was in good health and was grateful for it. He put it down to regular exercise and careful attention to diet (he restricted for example his intake of sugar). He still went on holiday each year to Alassio on the Italian riviera. Indeed pleasure in travelling was a constant theme in his life. He had a lot of happy memories to look back on associated with travel. Playing sport had also been an important element in his life—he had only given up tennis four years previously, 'because there was no-one to play with'.

I saw Mr Currie intermittently in the following ten years. His health remained very good, and he continued to go each year to Italy. Still very fit, he went swimming there. In his late seventies he surprised everyone in the housing scheme by buying a motor bike again, but he gave it up after two months when he realized his eyesight was not what it should be.

Ten years later at the age of 85–86 I spoke with him on three occasions and took the opportunity to question him again in detail on his attitudes to past and present. He expressed broadly similar attitudes to ten years previously but there was a significant difference. The emotional involvement he had displayed in reviewing his life had lessened. At the same time his judgements were clearer and often harsher. For example, he was sure now that he did not admire his father.

'He was hard. We had a hard bringing up. For instance, when we lived near Weymouth, Sundays my mother and father would walk along the cliffs and we would walk with them. We had to follow them behind, we couldn't get off the track. We were supposed to keep behind, it was Sunday ... My father was always such a busy man, he was obsessed with his work. I often wonder whether he didn't love his work more than he did his family ... My father was never a father after we left Weymouth. Business, business, business, work, work, work. He never took mother out. He was never a father to me. I could never sit on his knee or anything like that. He never played with us. Apart from my mother and sister, my younger life was not much good, nor theirs ...'

His regret about going into tailoring was also more sharply expressed. He had gone 'into the wrong job'. He was 'more mechanically inclined'. Looking at his life as a whole he said he saw no pattern, 'only craziness'.

Yet this very denial of meaning in the course his life had taken was expressed without bitterness, rather with a touch of humour. For despite the negative judgements on many aspects of his life, he had become more accepting of himself. Circumstances were often to blame for his failures. For example, he regretted less than he did his failure to marry. 'In those days one had to be able to keep a woman.' If anything was to blame it was the First World War which had taken a 'big chunk out of his life'. Moreover, he realized that after all he had 'never been very ambitious'. He had not been a one for responsibilities, and marriage was a big responsibility, particularly in the inter-war period. Maybe he had not got 'the important things in life', but then he had never really been in a position to get them.

He had had a lot of enjoyment. And it was the good things he thought back on now. Just as ten years previously he said he thought particularly about the 1920s after he returned from India when he had had a number of girlfriends. For the first time he showed me the photographs he still kept.

There was still an element of 'review' in his conversation but it was less marked. Certain things still troubled him, regret over the way he had treated his sister, and personal problems from his adolescence which he said he was glad to be able to talk over with someone at last without feeling criticized. Still most of the issues he had worried about ten years earlier seemed to have been resolved. He no longer used his father as a standard by which to judge himself. His father had not been such a good man. He had not been 'loving'.

A lessening of emotional involvement also showed itself in his attitudes to present society and to his present life. He saw people less now. His life was not as lively as in his youth, but he did not feel lonely as he had ten years previously. In fact he was glad to be on his own and liked his own company more. He could find enough things to interest him. He enjoyed watching sport on television, and playing his collection of records. But then from a child he had 'never known the meaning of boredom'. He had always been able to make his own pleasures.

His attitude to others was indicative of a certain degree of alienation. He put it in dramatic terms. He was 'losing respect for the human race'. When I put to him the comparison with his attitudes of ten years earlier he admitted that his views on society had become much more negative. People did not have the same commitment to one another. Men had forgotten how to work, women how to bring up children. Delinquent patterns of behaviour had been imported from America. But the crucial difference was that these attitudes were now expressed unemotionally, quite unlike ten years before. He was not proud to be British anymore. Previously he had said Britain was a 'great country' and had been 'worth fighting for'. Such thoughts had brought tears to his eyes. Now he was sure Britain was not worth fighting for, and he said this dry-eyed. (His subsequent reaction to the Falklands war of 1982 was also significant. The maintenance of British rule for a few islanders had not justified the loss of life. They could have been offered places in Britain.)

His major anxiety concerned what would happen to him in the future if his health deteriorated and he was worried about signs that he was slowing up. He would rather die than go into a home. As for the sheltered housing scheme where he had lived for almost 15 years and where the original warden was still in position, he did not like what he saw. The average age and disability of the residents had increased, but not the care they received. There would be nothing to complain about, he remarked, 'if the same care was taken of the residents as of the gardens!'.

The attitudes that Mr Currie expressed in the more than ten years that I spoke to him illustrate a number of interesting points. In the first place they show what the process of life review can mean. Since both in 1971 and 1981, Mr Currie showed signs of 'reviewing', it might be argued that it was a personality trait. But on his own admission reminiscing was something that he had begun to do only after his retirement, and there was distinct evidence of resolution of at least some of the thoughts that troubled him. Most of his major concerns about his past life had diminished by 1981. Indeed his attitude to the past had changed from being largely regretful to being largely accepting. But, and it is a point worth stressing, this 'development' did not mean he had come to possess 'integrity' in Erikson's sense. Both his growing sense of alienation from present society and his anxiety about what the future might bring, are attitudes quite contrary to those implied by 'integrity'.

In my last conversations with Mr Currie we spoke a lot about his anxieties for the future and I tried to reassure him about the services that were available. He looked forward greatly to my visits and the chance to talk. He was, however, unfortunate in his GP who had retorted, when he had gone 'for a check up' the year before, at the age of 88, 'what if everyone came asking for a check up!'. To a man of Mr Currie's sensitivity this remark had been very offensive and he had not been able to say what was on his mind. He had not visited his doctor since and felt unable to speak to him.

I encouraged him also to make contacts again with his relatives, his older sister's family, for example. He acknowledged that he had not been very forgiving, but said that it was too late now to make amends. I queried this. Happily though he had begun to make friends again among his neighbours, with one of whom he arranged joint shopping trips.

Miss Martin

Not all those who had negative attitudes to their past felt particularly guilty or regretful about their own actions. Some felt they had been the victims of misfortune beyond their control and sad memories dominated their thoughts. Miss Martin's memories were predominantly unpleasant and she said that she would disown them if she could. She thought back often on her life when she was alone and the story of her family's history gave her a sense of tragedy.

She had been born as an only child in Belgium in 1900 into a well educated Walloon family. Her father was a concert pianist, and the house when she was a young girl had 'always been full of artists'. Her father had been on many tours, especially to Russia. She closely identified herself with the 'bohemian' society she had mixed in when young. Free from values imposed from outside, but 'responsible':

'... I am a writer from heart, you see. Because all my people, my grandparents, were writers, my grandfather, and also my father with his music, he also used to write because it was in him. He should have been a writer, but he liked to be a musician as well ...'

This world suddenly disappeared in the First World War. Their house had been taken from them by Germans and she had witnessed scenes of great cruelty. Her mother had died, and she and her father had come to London as refugees.

But they had never been able to recover the same style of life. Happy memories of the good times before the war in the society of artists came to her still, but they were overshadowed by the events that followed.

When I first met Miss Martin she was living in one room in a basement of a large Victorian institution which had been converted for use as a sheltered housing scheme by the local district council. She had lived there for the last twelve years. The building was dark and forbidding and Miss Martin's room was cluttered with pieces of furniture piled one on top of the other and almost touching the ceiling. There was only a small passageway available for walking around the room, from the door to the chair to the bed to the sink and cooking unit. The epithet 'Dickensian' came readily to mind. When I used to visit I sat with her in a small corner of the room against the bed in the two chairs available. She had no pension. She relied on supplementary benefit to pay her rent and electricity. Yet she would still offer me wine from fine cut glasses, and this generosity she showed to the end of her life.

Miss Martin admitted that she was a 'collector', a 'bit abnormal'. Not only would she not dispose of any of her father's furniture, but she hoarded newspapers, magazines and other odds and ends which were piled in various spare spaces in the room, mainly under chairs and under the bed. Her father had died 18 years previously. She had worked for some years to support him, but in his last years she had given up work to look after him. They had had the support of a small circle of friends, mainly musicians.

Not long after her father's death, Miss Martin was diagnosed as having cancer for which she was operated on a couple of years later. This had left her weak, and when I met her her health was poor, with many rheumaticky aches and pains in her arms and legs. The doctor had told her she was depressed.

'... the world is rotten. I can't help it. I don't like the world. I told the doctor I wish I was courageous enough to take an overdose and finish with everything, because I'm fed up with the world, with everything. He said well, it's because you are depressed. He always gives me tablets for depression and they make me sick, they don't agree with me. Some of them I had to stop straight away because they didn't agree. He always thinks I am very depressed, I suppose he is right. I'm not a cheerful person, I know that...'

Certainly on the questionnaires I asked her to fill in, the MMPI Depression Scale and the Chicago Life Satisfaction Index, she answered more negatively than anyone else in my study. I remember the strong expression with which she said she 'hated old age'. She felt dissatisfied with her life and wished it could have been different, although she did not want to live another life. It was a pity that the one close friend she had made in life had now moved outside of London with her husband and so she did not see her anymore. But, she said, the problem was not that she was lonely, she did not wish for companionship. She stressed that it was the 'world' that depressed her.

She was happy to help me with my research and did not object also to filling in the long 16PF Cattell Personality Inventory. This brought out her 'assertive', 'uninhibited', 'imaginative' and also 'undisciplined' character. For indeed, although she was quiet and gentle in appearance she was bold in defending her values. She would speak out against unfairness in what she saw around her.

'... it's terrible to hear some people speak. I went and sat down there and some women will come and speak to you ... they said, "Look at all those foreigners, and all those black men, they take our women, they take our work, why don't they send them straight back". I said, "That's not all that easy ..." I said, "most of those blackies are British subjects, they can't stop them coming if they want to come and study here or work here ..." I said, "you've always been a free country. They come here, they think they are going to be free, to find work, to find a living, you can't blame them, most of them are coming for a reason." I wouldn't be here if I hadn't been a refugee, you see, so I can't blame them ... I know what it is to be in danger ...'

Her verdict on the life she saw around her was extremely negative.

'... it's the reaction of wars, I think, people are getting hard. They follow the slogan, I'm all right Jack, you can go to blazes, number one first. Of course there are a few nice people about, very kind, I know that, but I always say they are like a few lumps of sugar in the tea, it doesn't make the water sweet ...'

'... I think it is getting worse, and I think we haven't seen the worst yet. I feel very sorry for the new generation. When I see a woman pregnant today or with very small kiddies I think to myself, what are you going to be in the future, I don't see no future for them ...'

But the past was really no better.

'... I hear people speak about the "good old times". I think to myself, the good old times, my God, there's a lot of bad things today, but I wouldn't go back to the "good old times", it must have been awful, what they call the "good old times".'

Yet there was something mysterious to life, something too deep to understand. She thought of cruelty among animals. Humans were worst and the most violent beasts. She pondered whether there was any answer, any hope:

'... if the world changes at all in all those ways it will take millions of years as things are so deeply rooted. We won't see it anyway. I'm not religious, but I believe in Christ, something you see, you can put your hand on ... it's a marvellous book, the Bible is, but at the same time the writers didn't quite know what happened then, it was already too much of a long time after Christ, wasn't it, there's a lot of mystery there, that we will never know. But that's all I belive in, in Christ's precepts and ideals ... he was a man who wanted justice, he wanted the people to have a fair share in everything, that wasn't the ideal of the leaders of the country, of the capitalists you see, and that's why he got crucified. You see he was a revolutionary, he was a communist of his kind ... he was really a revolutionary person, and that's why I have always believed in him because I like his way of thinking. Because look how revolutionary he was when he was in the temple, he told the rich merchants to empty their sacks of goods which they got by the sweat of the poor people and told the poor people to take what you want, you see, well that's an awful revolutionary act, isn't it? I mean, he wouldn't be much liked for that, would he, and then there was another thing too, that a camel would get through the eye of a needle easier than a rich man, you see, a capitalist. I remember a Russian called Limpinoff, he was a sort of Russian minister. Anyway they went with teams of people round countries to see the different ways they managed their affairs, and he went into a school to see what a school was like and the teacher was just telling the pupils about this saying of Christ, and he said, "My God, fancy a capitalist country teaching things like that to the pupils, I can't get over it ..." and I sometimes hear things and I think, well that's rather daring, you know, saying those things. But there you are, people are opening their eyes day by day and getting cleverer, and what do you call it ... evolution.'

Although she said she reminisced, in fact Miss Martin spoke very little about the past to me. She spoke a lot about her present feelings and troubles in the world around, but she could not, or would not, construct stories about her past experiences. Perhaps this reflected her depressed attitudes to the past as a whole.

Miss Martin lived for another seven years, in which time I visited her eight times. In the first year her health became very poor and her mood was extremely depressed. The doctor had hinted she had cancer again and she had great difficulties walking out. As she looked out at the world she saw "the flames of hatred" in Ireland and elsewhere growing ever stronger. She saw no hope. But once I noted she did tell a long story of her past experience on a ferry boat between Belgium and England in stormy seas. All had seemed lost, but they had reached port safely.

Reminiscence in fact gradually became a more noticeable part of her conversation. She told me stories of her childhood in Belgium, of visits to Antwerp in particular. She spoke too of how they had left the country in the First World War. As I then knew I was going to work in Holland, our conversation often turned to the continent. How ugly she had found the Flemish language. Her mood improved somewhat despite a long episode in hospital after falling and breaking her leg. She was moved to another room vacated by a resident who had died, also in the basement, but much brighter. She was allowed to leave her furniture stored in the other room. She smiled at the new space she had to live in.

While I lived in Holland we corresponded at Christmas times. She was also befriended by another young man of French origins who lived locally and visited her regularly. They developed a close relationship and would speak French together. When I visited her in 1976 her health was still bad with problems from arthritis, especially in her legs, and her poor circulation. She was still melancholic and critical of the ignorance and prejudice in the world outside. She was dismayed at the attitudes of some of the other residents in the building who refused to have some help from coloured women. Yet there was a greater acceptance in her attitudes to her own past life. She did not seem to reject it as before. I noted how I was struck by her comment that she was glad she had been a girl and therefore had been able to look after her father in his difficulties. That seemed to be an affirmation of her life. She showed me photos of her father that she had not shown before, and programmes of his concerts. She gave me a tourist booklet he had brought back for her from Czarist Russia.

Two years later, when I saw her for the last time, she was housebound again and looked very ill. She felt bad inside and thought it was cancer again. She received home help and meals on wheels five days a week. Yet her sense of humour showed through more strongly than before. She could smile at her own misfortunes. Also there was a philosophical and poetic tone to a lot of what she said. She spoke about the sea again and its changing moods. 'Life goes so quick. You never know how nature will change.' She described a thunderstorm at sea appearing suddenly on a sunny day. She wished me well and hoped to see my 'new young family' one day. She told me how much she appreciated the friendship of the other young man who visited her regularly.

She sensed her own life was coming to a close. And now a lifetime did not seem so long, she said. She expressed appreciation for it. She could hardly believe her father had died over 25 years before. He had been such a good companion. Now she was old. Her view of the world remained pessimistic, but there was a twinkle in her eye that did not seem there before. She said that she tried to cheer herself up.

Three months later Miss Martin was admitted to a residential home for the elderly because her mobility had become so poor. She died a few weeks after going in, apparently from a heart attack.

Subsequent History of Other Cases

Mr Menash, Mr Currie and Miss Martin all moved subtly but nonetheless in clearly documented ways to a greater degree of acceptance of their past lives. They had not been able to put difficulties with the past behind them completely but their attitudes had became less negative. Mr Currie had moved the most, and certainly to a more pleasurable view of reminiscence. He liked now to look back on his happy memories and enjoy them as he had not been able to previously. For example, he could think of the girlfriends of his young days without regretting his failure to marry. He had had good times. His more positive view of his own past contrasted with a growing dislike of modern life. His attitude to society was certainly one of 'moral siege'. This was shown by his dramatic comment that he had 'lost respect for the human race'. His attitudes had become not dissimilar to those of some of the people discussed in the previous chapter. He had though been fortunate to maintain good health and this probably had some influence on his attitude to his own life, seen now from his late eighties. He had been fortunate to live so long and so healthily. Mr Menash's and Miss Martin's change of attitudes were objectively smaller but no less noteworthy for that, as more surprising and expressed in the face of growing disability and imminent death. They both in their own ways communicated a reconciliation with life before they died and a belief that life was good.

The other members of the group all died fairly rapidly after my initial visits and I did not see them all again. Mr Bennett died within two years. According to the warden's account his behaviour deteriorated, he became an alcoholic and did not look after himself. He was a 'nuisance' and was obliged in the end to move out of the housing complex. It seems very likely that his 'past' worries played a large part in his deterioration. When I last saw him he said they 'drove him mad'. Mrs Jones' mental disturbance also increased. In 1971 she was admitted to the psychiatric ward of her local hospital for two weeks because of what she described as a 'brainstorm'. According to the account she gave me she was found wandering outside the flats in her nightdress and locked herself in a neighbour's bedroom. Her doctor, she said, attributed her breakdown to 'accumulation of worry'. She attended the day centre at the hospital twice a week, and was full of praise for it. But when I saw her again later in the year, she was no longer attending the hospital but was again very depressed. She said she was very lonely and again very much wanted to die. She would like to commit suicide but thought it to be wrong as, she said, she 'believed in meeting her loved ones again'. She had fallen out again with her younger son over remarks that she made to him and was very upset about it. She felt abandoned. She said that the warden was harsh and unkind. She wished that the welfare services would send someone to see her but they had not responded to the contact she had made. Her memories were as much a source of worry as of comfort and she tried not to think back. She died two years later before I could see her again. According to her neighbour's account she also took to drink before she died and had to be helped in from the street once in a very disturbed state (it could have been though that it was only that she 'appeared' drunk as on the previous occasion).

Mr Thomson and Mr Gatting died within the year and I did not see either of them again. Both had found it very hard to bear their isolation, and thoughts about the past troubled them. The final person, Mr Elton, at the end of 1971 moved out of the housing complex which he hated so much and compared to his previous prison experience. I was unable to find out where he had moved to and therefore lost trace of him.

The total picture for this group of unhappy reminiscers is thus a mixed one. While positive change in attitude was possible and achieved by some, the most severely distressed received little or no help. As Butler has pointed out, the life review can have negative consequences for those who cannot achieve a satisfactory resolution of past conflicts. Success is by no means guaranteed.

The striking common image left in my mind is of the isolation and loneliness expressed by all of these eight people. Suicide was spoken of by a number as a possible escape from their situation and they debated its rights and wrongs. While it is possible to argue that an unhappy life situation, isolated from their previous contacts, within the sheltered housing scheme, and sometimes following the loss of their spouse (Mr Gatting, for example, had only lost his wife three years previously) aroused or exacerbated negative thinking about the past, it does seem more plausible to argue that the direction of influence was more from past to present. It has been said that loneliness 'has very little to do with lack of fellows and almost everything to do with an inability to be alone' (Kurtz, 1983). Loss of contact can be hard to bear but far worse is an inability to be content in one's own company. The individuals who have been described were no more objectively isolated than others in the study. Some did receive visits from family and friends, but far too few to satisfy them. Basically they disliked their own company. Their thoughts turned compulsively to the past and these thoughts worried them. It seems noteworthy that Mr Currie who came to enjoy his memories more over a period of ten years, described himself as being more content with his own company and not lonely anymore ten years later. Objectively he had become much more isolated from the world around. He saw far fewer people. But he felt less lonely. He enjoyed watching sport on the television and listening to his records, but he was also happier with his own thoughts.

The three cases studies that have been described in this chapter do not, I think, throw much light on the appropriate methods of helping people with disturbed memories, beyond the importance of being able to speak to an interested and sympathetic listener. But they do indicate its importance. The topic of counselling people with painful memories will be discussed further in Chapter 10.

Chapter 7

No Point in Looking Back

Distinguishing Characteristics

The general group of non-reminiscers, those who quite calmly told me that they saw no point in looking back, is the most heterogeneous of the four groups that I distinguished. As a young student with a career to make and an interest in demonstrating the value of reminiscence, to hear such answers was often disappointing. It was not consistent with the hypothesis that reminiscence was conducive to good adjustment in later life that apparently well adjusted people could say they saw no value in reminiscing. Human behaviour, however, is usually more complicated than most psychological hypotheses aim to be at outset, and achieving a greater degree of differentiation is itself a source of satisfaction. Indeed those who did not conform to my expectations by not reminiscing when they were expected to, revealed on further enquiry some of the most interesting points I discovered about adjustment in old age in the course of my research. They included people with quite diverse attitudes to their past and present lives. I have sub-divided them into four further groups.

Those who 'disappointed' me the most were those who reminisced a lot when I first met them but then did not want to say much more about their past lives in the following conversations. Three people behaved in this way. Mr Wickens was an imposing man of 91 years who gave me a detailed and rounded account of his life in my first interview with him, and drew a number of lessons from it. He expressed in well articulated terms a fatalistic view of life. Things happened beyond one's influence and expectations and altered the course of events inexorably. The first example of this in his own life, he said, was the paralysis of the brain that affected his mother when he was three years old. She lived a further 22 years in hospital but only remembered her son as a little boy. Mr Wickens had been ambitious. He had gone as a young man into the catering business and worked hard. He had worked closely with Billy Butlin's father. But bad health and accidents had intervened to prevent him being the success he could have been. He accepted it philosophically. 'That's fate.' He drew a number of other general lessons from his life experience. 'One can't put an old head on young shoulders,' he said. One must never assume that benefactors are anything other than out for their own ends—they will support and back one only when it suits them.

One must make the most of opportunities as they come along—'use anything if you can make something of it'. The integrated nature of his life history story suggested the completion of a successful life review process. Certainly, although he viewed himself as having been unlucky, he described himself as peaceful and reconciled to death. He said to me that he had told the doctor that he 'wanted to die'. He had 'seen enough', he 'had had his life'—a good innings.

I visited Mr Wickens quite a number of times, ten times altogether in the course of 1970 and 1971, but he never told me his life story again or really reminisced at any length, despite considerable pressing. His attitude was well expressed in his subsequent answer to the reminiscence questionnaire. Reminiscence had no point, he answered, there was 'no £.s.d' attached to it. He enjoyed very much speaking to me nevertheless. His room was full of knick-knacks—wirelesses, fans, clocks and various other odds and ends, and he liked to explain how things worked, refrigerators, tape recorders and so on. He enjoyed speaking also at length about politics and the merits and demerits of both Labour and Conservative policies. A competent man, despite his slowness of movement, it was he, the oldest tenant in the scheme, who was given charge when the warden and his wife were away. In such situations he more than once summoned the doctor to come to see another tenant.

In retrospect it seemed clear that he had told me his life story in detail initially as a way of telling me who he was. This of course is an important aspect of work with all older people, and social workers, for example, should be encouraged to take the time to let their clients introduce themselves in this way if they so wish. But at the same time it seems important to distinguish between this readiness and willingness to tell an interested listener one's life story by way of introduction, and a continuing interest in reminiscing about past times.

Mrs Williams responded to me in the same way. She was a lady of 88 years, badly crippled with arthritis and almost blind. But she coped remarkably well with maintaining her independent flat. She also gave me a fairly lengthy and integrated account of her life in the first conversation. She described her family background, a comparatively prosperous middle class one, and the visits she made to various relatives as a child. Her grandfather had built the local workhouse. She had been a very good pupil at school and wanted so much to be a schoolteacher, but her father died when she was still at school and as the family had no money anymore she had to go into service. From being a kitchen maid she had become a cook and married a coachman. His health was poor and she had to become the main breadwinner in the family. She had been a cook in various places, mainly at schools and other educational institutions. It was 'funny', she said, that she had always been in contact with teachers during her life. Even her present home help was an ex-teacher. She described her husband's last painful illness more than 40 years ago, how she prayed for his death because he was in such great pain, and how she 'missed him, even now'.

Yet on future occasions she did not want to go over the same ground again, and wanted to speak more about the present, about the details of her daily life, and about the talking books she received from the Blind Institute. In fact I pressed her too much with questions on reminiscence and she complained that I kept on the subject too much. She wanted to be 'cheered up!'. She did not want to reminisce and expressed the view that it 'did not serve much purpose'. Again like Mr Wickens she indicated an unlucky view of her life, but one with which she was quite reconciled. She liked to laugh at herself and her predicament.

Mrs Stanton too raised interesting issues about her past life when I first met her. She was 87 years old, spoke little and did not believe she could have much of interest to tell me. But to my questioning on reminiscing she told me in some detail how she had recently been through a period of asking herself why her mother had treated her so cruelly as a child. After her father died when she was eight, her mother had married again and made her the 'family drudge'. She wondered how her mother could have done it, to spoil her childhood in this way. Her life had been very bad indeed until she was 16 and managed to go to live with a friend at her mother's house. She resolved never to do the same to her own children. She therefore viewed her childhood as unhappy—unusual for the women in this sample who with very few exceptions looked back on childhood as a halcyon time—and she did not want to live her life over again for this reason. But on later occasions when we spoke she did not raise the topic again and indeed hardly spoke about the past. On the questionnaire about reminiscence she said she reminisced very little and saw it as having, 'no great role in her present life'. Yet her interior life was strongly developed. She read a lot, and she described books as 'taking her into another world'. She was also deeply religious. Her son took her every Sunday to their Baptist church and she said she 'lived with God'. She added that she believed not because she was afraid but because she 'loved Him'. Strikingly too, she expressed an appreciative attitude towards young people and the present world.

In each of the above three cases it seemed likely that the individual had been through a period of active life review and achieved some degree of resolution of past conflicts. As a result they had no further need to reminisce much. It is interesting that all were very old, 91, 88 and 87 respectively. Lieberman and Tobin in their large-scale study of adjustment to old age, report a strong link between great age and low introspection and suggest that 'a low level of introspection characterizes the old-old because the majority of them have already accomplished a life review and show signs of resolution' (Lieberman and Tobin, 1983 p.290). None of these three people expressed a predominantly positive attitude to their past lives, but they appeared resigned to it and their morale was neither particularly high nor particularly low.

Somewhat different were those who also indicated a dissatisfied attitude to their past lives and who expressed no form of resolution, but yet spoke of reminiscence as unimportant to them. A good example of this set of attitudes was Mr Sapper. Only 72 years old, he was very dissatisfied with his life in general. His wife had died two years previously and he regretted greatly moving away from his old surroundings. He spoke little about the past, but he did reveal that he had spent a period in prison for stealing from a gas meter. He did not want to speak about it, though. He said he did not reminisce much, that it did not give him a good feeling and that most of his memories were unpleasant ones. He was very suspicious of other people and therefore would not go to clubs, and was generally pessimistic in his attitudes. He was kind to me, though expressing the opinion that I certainly would not be able to make sufficient sense of old people's lives to write a book about the subject! Once he asked me how I was getting on and added, 'You can't put it all together properly, that's my opinion!'. He complained of poverty, how he had to economize on coal and expressed with some feeling that he would be 'better off in prison'. His one friend was his budgerigar whom 'he did not know what he would do without'. He seemed to successfully defend himself from trying to make sense of his own life and most of his conversation focussed on present concerns, as hooligans down the street and problems with the warden and other tenants.

Two other people expressed similar attitudes. Mrs Ball's attitudes were very similar indeed. Not only did she express dissatisfaction with both present and past life and attribute no importance to reminiscence, but she also complained greatly of life within the housing scheme and wished she had never left her old neighbourhood. Like Mrs Stanton she referred to an unhappy childhood with strict parents. Before coming to the housing scheme, however, she had had a busy life, always being out and about. Now she felt confined both by her legs and by where she lived. Mr Charles too disliked the way he had slowed up in recent years, which prevented him going out to the various sporting fixtures he enjoyed. Like the previous two people he was dissatisfied with his past and present lives, and did not reminisce.

All these six non-reminiscers then expressed noticeable dissatisfaction with their past lives. The former three, however, had appeared to resolve any difficulties they might still feel and were more reconciled with their lives, while the latter three were defensive and unhappy. None of the six survived long after my initial study and therefore their quite distinct attitudes are not represented in the case studies that follow, and this should be borne in mind in interpreting their significance.

The remaining nine people all expressed more or less positive attitudes to their past and present lives, but did so without attributing much importance to reminiscence. The most commonly expressed philosophy of life was of 'keeping going', and the importance of this was stressed equally by both older and younger people. Mr Butcher was only 68, single and recently retired. He kept up his interest in fishing, travelling and local politics and helped the warden of the housing scheme with clerical work. Mrs Topps was 88 with quite severe arthritis and mobility problems. Still, she would not give up her attendance at a day centre quite some distance away. She, in fact, had helped to set up this particular day centre when she was younger, and though she had now moved out of the area (which she regretted) she struggled to get there nonetheless. Old people, she said, must have 'spirit' and keep going. They must have 'willpower' and not take notice of difficulties. Laughter was a great boost. Reminiscing on the other hand she thought did not help much.

Mrs Emery expressed similar views. She was 91 and had no arms, since falling under a train when she was 64. Much admired by everybody, she kept up her independence remarkably well. The warden helped her with preparing food and dressing. She had a special stand for reading and claimed to read nine books a week. She kept an open door and was regularly visited by friends in the locality where she lived. It was difficult in fact to catch her on her own. Still, she said, 'she would exchange a leg for an arm'. She dismissed the value of reminiscing. Just as for Mrs Topps it would have been a sign of defeat for her.

Mrs Ditton had also displayed remarkable courage in her life. At first appearance mild looking, she was in fact a strong and forceful person. Eighty-six years old, housebound and with severe angina, she was still very much in control of her life. She looked people straight in the eye and, she said, 'stood no nonsense'. She had criticized the housing manager 'to his face' for deficiencies in the housing scheme. In service between the ages of 11 and 20, which she described as a good grounding for life, she had then married and had six children. But the First World War brought big changes for her. Four of her brothers were killed and her husband was badly gassed. Moreover, because he left the army hospital against orders, they did not receive a pension. He was ill for the remaining 16 years of his life. Mrs Ditton had to bring up six children by her own labour and like Miss Brown's mother she had refused all invitations to have any put into a home. She had succeeded. Her attitude to her success was religious. She believed in the power of God's help to be obtained through prayer, and in the strength that He gave her to survive misfortune. In more recent times she had survived blows, as the death of her son after an ear infection spread to his brain and a burglary in her old house. Each had a path to follow, she said, but God was there to help. She maintained a strong attachment to her family and one of her children or grandchildren came to see her every day. She was still very much the mother of the family.

She was happy to help me with my research and most co-operative with questionnaires and tape recordings. Yet at the same time she was quite definite in her denial of the value of reminiscence. Strikingly so, considering she had a lot in her life to look back on and be proud of. She thought it was important for old people to live in the present, with their families, and take an interest in what was going on in the world around them. She herself was highly critical of modern trends, of poor parenting, of increasing immorality and crime, but her attitude was active and combative rather than 'siege-like'. She was highly critical of other old people who reminisced a great deal and cut themselves off from the present. She thought this was 'bad for the brain'. To dwell too much on her own past for example, she said, would not be sensible. It would 'worry her mind' to dwell on the difficulties she had had, and divert attention from her present life.

Within this group of non-reminiscers there was a further sub-group of three women whose attitudes and lifestyle were very similar. They all had very positive attitudes to old age and had very high morale. All three commented that they were glad to be free of some of the ties that had previously held them. They liked their own company and had particular hobbies, sewing and handicraft in particular, for which they had little time in earlier life. Mrs Taylor, for example, said she had had to work hard from the time she was a child. Her husband had lost his work in the 1920s and she had had to become the breadwinner. They had had no children. After her husband's death in a bombing raid in the Second World War, she had lived with a niece for 14 years and had constantly been 'ordered around'. She had been glad to leave when the opportunity came to go and live as a companion to another widowed lady, which she had done for six years. But now at last to have a flat of her own and 'no-one to tell her what to do,' she said, made this the happiest time of her life. She enjoyed decorating the room with her own sewing work, a pleasure in home making she had never known before. She was 86 years old.

Mrs Tooley, 74 years old, also had gone to live with her daughter when her husband died and stayed there for nine years. 'It did not do,' she said, 'to live with relatives.' Since they had separated she and her daughter were now better friends. She enjoyed her present life and was not lonely. As with Mrs Taylor, shopping and making things nice in her flat were great pleasures for her. She expressed particularly strong views against reminiscing. She had purposely 'destroyed all' her photos when she came to live in the sheltered housing scheme—an action in which she seemed to have turned her back on the past and which she said she did not regret in the least. Yet at the same time she expressed herself satisfied with her past life and seemed well content.

The third lady in this group, Mrs Faith, lived the longest, and is the subject of the first case study in this chapter. Her case well illustrates the sense of liberation that can be experienced with the new found freedom of later life. Reminiscence, looking back, appears irrelevant to Mrs Faith, quite understandably so in the context of her life history. The present is far more absorbing to her. The other two cases, detailed in this chapter, that of Mr Lothian and Miss Norman, illustrate the importance for many people in old age of maintaining continuity of lifestyle—the most commonly expressed attitude among those who rejected the value of reminiscence. Looking back for such people often seemed synonymous with 'giving up'.

But perhaps just as important as their wish to continue as before, such people expressed a different value orientation to memory. Mr Lothian, for example, had good stories to tell from the past, but he did not appreciate that they could be a valuable asset to himself or to others. Paradoxically he did not discard the interest of history. In fact he read avidly historical accounts of past events—but he did not seem to see his own memories in the same light. It should be remembered of course that the upsurge of interest in social history and the encouragement of oral history that are such remarkable characteristics of the 1980s are comparatively recent developments. Few of the people in the present study, however—Mr Cook in Chapter 5 is one exception—lived long enough to enjoy the benefits of this re-evaluation of old people's memories.

Mrs Faith

Mrs Faith was a quiet, smartly dressed woman who looked much younger than her 80 years. She lived in a new sheltered housing scheme in Marylebone. Her room was well furnished and had a well kept and comfortable appearance about it, with many cushions embroidered by Mrs Faith herself. She liked to give me tea with cakes, usually home-made. A shy lady, she felt herself to be 'not much of a conversationalist'. Indeed she was somewhat surprised yet pleased that I wanted to visit her. She would ask sensitively 'I hope I am not boring you?' Two years later she said that my visits 'had brought her out'. It seemed a lot to say for such a little—seven relatively short visits. But in fact this comment seemed to reflect how in may respects life had blossomed unexpectedly in old age. She went out more, had more interests and more social life generally than when she was younger. Not surprisingly, therefore, she had a very positive attitude to old age.

She had been born on the south bank of the Thames opposite St Thomas's hospital near Waterloo. She described herself as a 'real Londoner'. Her grandfather had been the head boilerman at the Houses of Parliament, and retired with a pension of a pound a week, 'a lot in those days'. Her own father had also worked 'for government'.

'... my father used to go to the different buildings, Clarence House, Marlborough House, St James's, and repair the gilding on the ceiling. Sometimes it would break away and my father took the gold leaf and used to fill in all the cracks. He had to go to all the different palaces, just touching them up. So you see my father had a lot of patience doing that ...'

Mrs Faith was patient too, and she said a number of times to me that she 'took after' her mother and father. They were 'patient, too busy to talk much'.

Mrs Faith had also followed her father's interest in artistic handwork and had developed early a lifelong interest in sewing and embroidery. She started a career when she left school.

'... I started work at dressmaking, that's why I'm very good with my needle. I was apprenticed in Bond Street, and I walked over the bridge, Westminster Bridge, and if I got across the bridge when it was striking eight o'clock I knew I'd be in time, that gave me half an hour to get there by half past eight, half past eight in the morning, and we worked till nearly half past eight in the evening for half a crown ...'

But Mrs Faith had given up her career when she married and the circumstances of her later married life in particular had been restricting and isolating. She had married after the First World War and their one son was born soon afterwards. Her husband had worked first as a chauffeur for some time to a Harley Street surgeon. In the late 1930s he could find no more work and had to take a job as a porter in a block of flats in Knightsbridge where they lived right through the second war. With most of the other porters called up for military service, Mr Faith virtually ran the block, but after the war they all came back to reclaim their jobs and Mr Faith moved with his wife to a joint husband and wife caretaker's job in Wimpole Street. Her husband had later become disabled and in 1954 they had moved again, with Mrs Faith being the sole caretaker, to a large house in Devonshire Street. Her son, an organist and music teacher, had by now moved out of London with his own family and lived on the Kent coast. Mrs

Faith had finally retired in 1964 when she was 73. By this time her husband was very ill. They had put their names down for council housing and were allocated a place in a just completed scheme, near to where they had previously worked in Wimpole Street. Mr Faith died there the following year.

After her husband's death Mrs Faith had started going out again and she now went out much more than previously, to adult education handicraft classes in particular, which she enjoyed very much, and to afternoon meetings at the local church. She commented on the differences in her life.

'... you see, when you are in caretaker jobs you are isolated, there's nobody, unless you happen to see the housekeeper next door. But it might be a month, and you might never meet her, you were isolated you see ...'

'... I have more contact now. I go to these sewing classes and we are friendly whilst we are there. It just stops at that you see, but I see a great many people. You see, when you live in a basement you really are right away from everything ... as I said to the minister, when you are in those jobs you are working Sundays as well to keep the central heating going and you've no time for church, you've no time at all, not in those jobs, seven days a week ...'

The handwork which had now become so important for Mrs Faith had been an underlying interest all her life. She had made her own dresses and chaircovers, but now there was a lot to make, cuddly animals, cushions and dresses for the church Christmas bazaar. A lot of ideas had been stimulated too by the teacher of the adult education classes. She showed what old people were capable of.

'... you should see the paintings too. You would be amazed that elderly people had done them and some had never painted before ...'

Reminiscence was comparatively unimportant to Mrs Faith. She said she neither spoke nor thought much about the past.

'... I don't seem to have time for it. It's only if in conversation or we've seen anything on TV we'll say, oh do you remember that, for instance about the new coins or what we used to get for a penny, and then it just goes on you see, you just happen to talk about it, but that's not dwelling on the past. When I sit alone here, I really couldn't tell you what I'm thinking about, that's funny. I probably might be thinking about my sisters or my son or what work, what sewing I've been doing ...'

Her orientation was towards the present and reminiscing she saw as not 'concentrating' on the present, and therefore an inappropriate use of time.

She looked forward to the spring, to more daylight for sewing and going out.

'... the daylight is wonderful you see, the light evenings ... with the electric light I can't thread a needle you see. I do quite a lot in the summer then I like to go out as well, two things I like the light for, sewing and I like to go out. Really I don't have time to think about the past.'

There was no particular pattern or meaning in her life as she understood it, re-markable enough to deserve more than a passing comment or thought.

'... so I've come back to where I started, because you see he had a job in Wimpole Street and we came right back again, so that's our life. But I never think any more about it. You know sometimes if you pass a house that you know, you do ...'

Mrs Faith was a meticulous person and she took care to answer my questions on reminiscence as carefully as she could. The night her husband died, she said, she had reminisced a lot. She had spoken for hours with the warden about how she met her husband, about their courtship and so on. But this was the 'only time' she could think of. When I visited her she hardly ever spoke about the past, and if she did, it was mainly about her parents, in particular her father's work as a painter. Her own handwork absorbed her completely, and she always had something new to show me that she had made or was making. She spoke a little too about current affairs, fashions in clothing, and the problems of other older people. For example, she believed in euthanasia:

'... I really think in a case like that it would be release if they were taken when they are forgetful and can't remember—you know they get bothering other people and that kind of thing—I wish it myself. The doctor could give you a sleeping pill. I would wish it ... yes it's a difficult question. I wouldn't want to be a bother to anybody really. I do think of course they lay and suffer, some of them do, and the nurses that are in charge of them, they know that they'll never get better and they can do nothing about it. It's very sad really, isn't it.'

Her attitude to the present day was a tolerant one. Indeed in many ways the present was preferable to the past, which matched her own experience of life's changes. Life today was 'totally different'.

'... for one thing, the people I mix with are more friendly you know, easier to get on with. I'm referring to the church people of course. There are some that are different to others and have better positions but I mix with them and they are very nice people, whereas if I can remember in my younger days they would scarcely speak to you, you know ...'

She remarked how the Second World War had opened many people's eyes to class differences. The previous head porter of the block of flats where Mrs Faith's husband had worked during the war did not want his old job back when he returned. 'After he had been to war he could see the different side to things.' Work like portering was demeaning to him.

She found a greater friendliness too in the shops. For instance she did not worry about her difficulties in understanding the new decimal coinage.

'We'll get used to it I except in time, they are very helpful in the shops ...'

Above all welfare services were much improved.

'They are more interested in you nowadays ... much more is done for you. The welfare service is very good. They provided the materials for us to do sewing at the day centre and there's a chiropodist there too if you want to have your feet attended to. Also you can go and have a meal there. You needn't cook your lunch. You can go and have a meal ... oh yes, there's a lot to be thankful for.'

She felt that contemporary young people were not so polite as in her days but she had good words to say about them too.

'... I think the younger generation are more impatient but the teenagers are more ready to help nowadays, they are more understanding, they are more ready to do things than perhaps in my days, perhaps because of education ...'

All in all Mrs Faith gave the impression of someone not afraid to appreciate the opportunities a new life gave her. She lived in the present and did not want to be tied up by any nostalgic feeling for the past or regret that opportunities had not come earlier. Perhaps she had always taken things in the same accepting, patient ways. The work she did with her hands, however, did provide a thread of continuity through her life back to her childhood and her parents. Since her activities were time consuming there was just not the time for reminiscing. When it came to relaxing in the evening she liked to watch the TV.

Mrs Faith lived another seven years and I saw her on five occasions in that time. Her health remained good and she was able to continue her sewing and embroidery right to the end. She did, however, suffer a grievous blow when her son died five years before her own death. But she recovered and on later occasions spoke with interest of her grandson who had visited her. She had also continued going to stay with her sister for holidays.

When I visited she did not speak about the past with me, but I was surprised once when she told me that she had entered a competition on 'memories' at the day club she attended. She had written an essay on a 'Childhood Jubilee' in which she remembered her experiences of Queen Victoria's jubilee. She had enjoyed doing it and her writing had been much appreciated. But it was her handi-work—always with a new project as focus—which continued to absorb her the most. When I last saw her in the year before she died, aged 87, it had been over three years since we had met, but she remembered me well. Apart from being a bit unsteady on her feet, she looked the same. Her room was neat and tidy. She gave me tea and cakes and showed me her embroidery as before. She was still going to the day club. Her doctor, she said, praised her for her activity. She died a few months later, suddenly in her sleep, from a heart attack. She acknowledged that living in the present in the way she did was a great gift: '... now the days are getting lighter, I shall probably make a new dress, you see that all keeps my mind on everday.'

Mr Lothian

Mr Lothian was a single man of 80, a 'loner', of short build, and as he proudly said, 'a Scot'. He was somewhat deaf. His room had a rather scruffy appearance but it had probably always been the same. When I arrived he would be seated at his small table with the same stained tablecloth, the ketchup bottle and a copy of the *News of the World*. The women in the sheltered housing scheme where he lived talked pityingly of him as, 'the poor man upstairs who hasn't got a soul in the world'. But Mr Lothian would not have felt any need for sympathy—he felt he was all right as he was, and indeed better equipped to deal with life than most. He said to me he was glad he was not married and took care to avoid going on coach trips to the coast with the rest of the, mainly women, tenants in the house. His appearance was slightly aggressive. He was suspicious of me and my questions to begin with, but once he got to know me he was pleased for me to visit. 'See you again,' he would always say as I left, 'look after yourself.' There was always too a sparkle in his eyes. He chuckled a lot to himself.

He had left Edinburgh, where he was born, in 1917, but he would never speak about his family or other personal matters. To my questions on reminiscence he usually changed the subject, but in his general conversation he gave some hints of his tough background.

'... bringing up families in those days, there was not all this money they're earning now, there was no dole. If you were out of work you had no money unless you had saved a bob or two. Things were cheap it's true, but not all that cheap. If you wanted a suit of clothes made to measure it would cost you that week's wages and some on top you know ... pair of shoes, pair of boots, five bob, that's five bob out of your wages ...'

'...Edinburgh used to be terrible in the old days ... rough places there too ... it wasn't safe walking down an alley if you had any money in your pockets ...'

'... I served a five year apprenticeship [as a sheet metal worker] in Edinburgh ... I started at tuppence an hour, that's nine and a half hours a day and six hours on a Saturday. We started at six o'clock in the morning and worked until nine o'clock and then from nine till ten was breakfast time, then you started at ten until one o'clock, that was the next break, one till two, then from two till half past five ... They say they work harder now, I don't know where! "The hardship today is terrible," I don't know where, I can't see hardship, can you? ...'

'... there were no women working like there is today, the only women you might see were old women about 60 or 70 ... and yet people lived, didn't they?'

'... when you reached a certain age they used to put you in the workhouse, and you were in there and you had to work, chop wood up, do sweeping up and all that sort of thing, no wages, you didn't get no wages for that you know, just your food, that's all, and your bed. In one place you might chop wood up, another place you might be a shoemaker, repairer, repair the boots and shoes, but no wages ...'

He was aware of how easily violence could erupt in society, and of the need to keep alert to danger. He had vivid memories of unemployment and social anarchy in the inter-war years, of being out of work and long walks to find jobs. He seemed to have read a lot as well about the origins of the Second World War. He could see the same signs now.

'. . . Ninety thousand short of a million . . . by Christmas time it will be over a million unemployed I reckon, the way they are going on. It's bad in Scotland too, the Clyde isn't it. They want to be careful what they are doing up there. They don't stand no nonsense there. They didn't in the 1930s you know. It was terrible. They raided every shop in Glasgow, nearly. Grocers' shops. Not one or two men, but about 50, armed, went into the shops. "Come on all out with the stuff. Out with it, the lot. Come on." The pubs too. All cleared of whisky . . . grocers' shops, butchers' shops, they smashed all they wanted to get in . . . the police couldn't do nothing. They were helpless. Suppose there were a dozen over there doing a shop, another 20 here doing it, and then people in their houses, do you know what they were doing, they were opening their windows, hurling things down amongst the police . . . you'd hear no more again for another week providing they got work of some description. It was all right then. Some of them had no rent paid, and the landlords couldn't do anything. If they said anything they would smash all the place up. Break all the windows, they wouldn't care . . . It'll get the same again if they are not careful. There's 60,000 dockers on the docks you know. That's a lot of men, isn't it? You get them nasty! They've got money in their pockets at the present time, that will keep them going. It's got to be pretty bad before they do it. See, it's up to Heath [the Prime Minister] to see to these things. That's what he's there for, isn't it!. . . After a slump there'll be a war. I expect that will be the next thing. With Russia. We'll know all about it then, won't we? . . . That will stop it all. That's what they'll do . . . They'll be sorry for it presently, all this . . .'

But the battles he liked to speak about most were his daily struggles against being cheated.

'I gave him a fiver and he gave me change for a pound. I said, "What about my change?". He said, "I gave you your change." I said, "I gave you a five pound note". He said, "I'm sorry". I said, "I'm not". I said, "I come from Scotland . . ." He said, "I didn't mean to do it". I said, "No, nobody means to but they do, don't they . . ." You've got to watch them!'

'I gave the milkman a shilling for some biscuits. He said, "They've gone up". I said, "Look here, you had them lying in your van last week. The same thing. How's it gone up. What are you talking about?". They'd cheat you out of a penny if you're not careful . . .'

The new decimal coinage that had been introduced provided many opportunities for 'cheating'.

'. . . a lot of people are being robbed you know, do you know that, older people. See they don't know what that coin value is. They don't know it's worth a penny. They can't see unless someone tells them . . . I gave the milkman three of them new twopenny pieces—they're the same as five old pennies—and he gave me one half-penny piece back, which is the value of an old penny. So I said to him, 'What's this?'. He said, 'Your change'. I said, 'I want another two'. I said, 'How much is the milk?' He said 'One [shilling] and a penny'. I said, 'Well I gave 15 old pennies worth'. Oh he argued about that, that was the second time he tried that with me. But I got it. I said, 'It's rightfully mine, not yours. And another thing, you gave me a new penny piece one day. Sometimes it can be the value of twopence and sometimes it can be threepence.' He said, 'That's right'. I said, 'It's not right!'. I said, 'Look when I give you one of these penny pieces, you tell me it's only worth twopence, but," I said, "When you give it to me you tell me it's worth threepence. Can you account for it," I said. "Come on, let's have it." He didn't know what to say. I got him beat . . . That's how you've got to catch him, he does that with all of them, the old women, they are being cheated out of pennies . . . it wants stopping, that caper. It was in the paper the other day about it, about these traders doing that and cheating people. I can't afford it. I said to him, "Look supposing I had a silver five penny piece and that was all I'd got and I wanted a small loaf of bread. Well say the bread cost one shilling and a penny. I'll put it that way." He said, "Yes". I said, "I wouldn't get that loaf because I'm a penny short, because you've got it in your pocket when actualy it belongs to me. Right?" He didn't know what to say. I'd got him shocked there all right, he don't cheat me now, he gives me the right change ... I said, "All you've got to do now is give me three half-penny pieces which are the value of a penny each ... that will do me for three-pence change. I don't want a new penny, which is a two-penny piece, because, I'll tell you why, if you put one of these half-penny pieces which is a penny with two penny pieces which are tuppenny pieces, that's five-pence—but it should be the value of a six-pence." I said, "I don't need to tell you that, because you know that without me telling you. You know all about that. You know more than I do about it". I said, "I don't want none of the fiddling". He didn't know what to say ...'

He saw old people as being particularly vulnerable to exploitation—even in an old people's home. He had heard recently from an old acquaintance.

'... he went into an institution about three years ago. He told me he had about 15 shillings in his pocket and he handed his pension book over, he got a certain amount back you know, when pay day came round. He was there two nights and he was having a bath one morning and one of the attendants came in and started searching his pockets. He said, "You've got my pension book, so why do you want to search my pockets?". He said to me, "I don't care who they are or what they are," he said, "that's stealing". It is you know, isn't it ... he lives now with his son. Must be about 74 or 75 now. His son said he was mad when he went in that place. "What do you want to go there for when you can come and live with us." I met him one day after that. "How are you", I said. "All right," he said. "I've got a room to myself." He keeps some of his pension now in his pocket...'

His concern about the dangers of trickery made him sometimes contemplate drastic solutions.

'... sometimes I think you'd be better off with communism. You wouldn't have to worry about money then. There'd be none to steal from, would there ... there would be nothing to steal. They might pinch your dinner if you're not careful though ...'

'... in the shops this morning 18 shillings a pound for steak. She wouldn't have it. I shouldn't think so either. Robbery that is you know, don't you think ... I think the government should take all these shops over and sling them out of it, then they'd be run by the government. You'd know what you were getting then. They'd only be employees, not managers, that's what they should do with those people ...'

He was proud of himself both in the past and the present. He had had a tough life and survived. Although he did not want a return to the violence and anarchy of the pre-war days, he resented the demands of the present working class who wanted much more than old people, who had had to work really hard for what they got and now had to struggle to survive.

'... strikes ... you've got to pay for all of that. Busmen, they want another rise. They say they want five pounds. Now they are getting 22 pounds and they say they want to make their money up to 28. Well the public has got to pay for that. What do you think of that?

... Put them on the same level as us people, that's the way to do it. If we can do it, they can do it. That's all they've got to do. Let them work or starve. See how they like that ...'

'... the same as the post strike. They should have gone back with that 9 per cent and then asked for another increase in a few months' time ... no, they want it all at once ... yet people before the '14 war, skilled men, could be a plumber, a coppersmith, tinsmith, blacksmith, all got about 30 bob, 35 bob a week the limit. Not even two pounds, yet all this money they are earning and can't live, it seems ridiculous don't it?...'

'... I remember the time I was working down in Thames Ditton, years ago now, things were bad and I couldn't get the money I wanted. He said, "I'll pay you that but no more," he said, "that's all I'm going to pay, one and fourpence halfpenny an hour". I said, "That's not much is it". There you are, take it or leave it. I was wanting to have one and eight, but the slump was on, you couldn't do much about it, you had to take it see ...'

'... a lot of them today are not skilled, half of them call themselves skilled, yet they've only been labourers working for Tom, Dick and Harry, rubbish isn't it. To be skilled properly you've got to serve an apprenticeship, you've got to know something to be skilled. I mean now, I'm a sheet metal worker, supposing I started a job, a man might come up and say to me, I want you to make that, give you a sketch of what he wants and might give you the metal. There's nobody shows you, so if you can't do it, it's no good starting the job, is it, and a fool would start to try and do something he knew nothing about, wouldn't he?'

'... one day I was making some necks for petrol cans, necks where you pour the petrol in, made of brass tubing ... I put them in the stores and he got one of these young blokes in to solder the necks onto the tanks. And they were not soldered properly ... he said, 'Did you put these necks on these tanks?'. I said, 'Me, no'. 'Well', he said, 'you made the necks.' I said, 'I made the necks, but I didn't put them on the tank'. I said, 'You want to find out some of these blokes you've taken on, not me'. This bloke had put them on and when the customer took the cap off the neck came away from the tank. It wasn't soldered properly. He thought he could solder I suppose, he had seen somebody doing something and though he could do it too ... it's all skilled work. You've got to know what you are doing. The same as these men in the streets putting paving stones, sticking up in the corners like this, that's not right, is it, it should be level. There should be no such thing as sticking up, it should be as level as that table with nothing sticking up. If it's not down properly, some time should be taken to see that it is down. A bit of cement put in the corner of each of these slabs and stuck there ...'

I saw him eight times in the first two years I got to know him. He liked talking. The stories, although always different, had common themes: in particular violence and crime and solutions to them. He spoke of the way prisons were run and the police, punishments and tortures, both in the past and present. He was an avid reader of newspaper accounts of robberies and court cases. He liked to read detective stories too, and he usually had a new paperback that he was reading. He also spoke a lot about politics, national and international. He was particularly critical of the attempts to get Britain in the Common Market. He was convinced it would lead to poorer standards of food and much more expensive food. Often he would criticize the present working man for lower standards of workmanship that would have earned the sack in the past, and excessive wage demands. But he had to admit that life was better today for the average working man, but this had not necessarily produced a better society.

'... as far as living conditions today, I think there is a big improvement. The only thing is there's more crime today. That wants stopping, doesn't it. I think they are going to make new laws. The sooner we get it done the better we'll like it. Hooligans, thugs and all that ... the birch, prison sentences, long ones ...'

Of himself he gave little away deliberately and would never answer direct questions about his past life or his present conditions. 'I'm all right,' he would say, 'nothing to grumble about' ... 'I don't worry till worry worries me.' The talk of whisky brought a gleam to his eyes. They were the only 'spirits' he had ever seen!

'... a bottle of whisky was half a crown a bottle. Whisky 90 proof, seven years old. It's about two years old now, and you saved all that money ... it's more of a medicine than anything else, it wasn't meant to drink, like a national drink ... at one time you had to have a certificate to get it in a public house, you know ... "Who's it for? What's it for?" and all that, you know. "All right, give him a bottle or half a bottle." ... A bottle of whisky you know would kill you, if you drink enough of it for very long ...'

Mr Lothian lived another four years, in which time I saw him on three occasions, and he continued to give the impression of someone coping well with life's problems, while forecasting disaster all around—the loss of freedom that the Common Market would bring and the dangers of nuclear war with Russia. He remained in good health. His self esteem was striking: 'I can read between the lines' ... 'no education but plenty of brains' ... 'tell them I'm a Scot'. With tongue in cheek he attributed his 'pep' to eating OK sauce neat.

He talked mainly about politics: about drastic solutions to deal with the IRA in Ireland, about crime and traffic (he had been in hospital for a short stay in 1972 after being knocked down by a car in the road outside) as well as interpretations of history, the Second World War in particular. With his £10 Christmas bonus he had bought a bottle of whisky and got drunk. He laughed about it. He had even had to call the firemen. Yet the last time I saw him he was scathing about the 'expert' whom he had seen quoted in the newspaper recommending old people to live dangerously so as not to be a burden on others. 'Why doesn't he cut his own throat! ... old people have paid their taxes all their lives.'

For all his aggressive front and his vigorous independence he did care about other people and the way they were treated. Fairness and justice were vital in life. Old people deserved better. His anger was directed against villains, and he was genuinely concerned for the old women around him, lest they be cheated, even though he did not care for their company. Life had taught him some lessons, and they needed to be constantly applied. One had to keep guard. He took an interest in me that sometimes surprised me. Once he gave me advice on a projected visit to Russia.

'... don't take your camera whatever you do ... be careful what you say, don't run it down. Once you do that, they've got you, don't do that, not there. I wouldn't go to a place like that myself. You're never sure what's going to happen ... it might be all right, I wouldn't like to say. No, you can't depend on that.'

Miss Norman

Miss Norman was born in a town near Newcastle on Tyne in 1902. She came from a large family of twelve children. Her father ran a newsagents shop and on her own account damaged her hearing as a child 'standing in a draught in the shop'. Both her parents died young and the family had to split up. A number of the children came south as there were more possibilities than in the north. Miss Norman and her twin sister went to work in service. She moved a lot from one place to another, and was housekeeper for a number of well-to-do families. She worked last in a restaurant with her sister in a suburb of London where I met her. In 1962 she was hit by a car in the road and gave up work as a consequence. A few years later she moved into sheltered housing. Her sister also lived in the same housing complex.

I spoke with Miss Norman five times altogether in the course of 1970 and 1971 when she was 69 years old. Her health was good, she had no disability apart from her hearing loss, for which she wore an aid. She said she could do all that she liked to do. Her main contacts were with her sister, and they did many things together, especially walking and shopping. She also saw a lot of her brothers, who lived nearby. She was active too in going out to see various friends.

Although cheerful and friendly and quite open in expressing her views about the people around her, Miss Norman would say little about her own past life. In answer to direct questionning, she said she was satisfied with what she had done in her life and that her memories were more pleasant than unpleasant. There were some things she would have liked to have been different, but she had had no great expectations in life. Her past did not concern her. She said she did not think much about it, and indeed it hardly entered her conversation at all. Sometimes she said she wondered what would have happened if she had done things differently, but generally she did not bother about the past. Reminiscence 'served no purpose'.

Whenever our conversations did touch on the circumstances of her life, her comments seemed casual:

'... I just moved on from one job to another you know. Oh, I've been around.'

She'd worked for a time in Ireland, but being brought up as a Wesleyan she did not like the Catholic practices there.

'... I went over with some people I was working for. But I didn't feel settled. I wasn't one of them, do you see what I mean. I didn't like it when 12 o'clock came and they used to cross themselves. I didn't like it, not being one of them.'

She liked it best in the country of her birth up north.

'... they're more sociable, the door's always open up there, there's always a cup of tea for you. Down here, they are stuck up ... it's very cold up there though, but it's more sociable, you know, it makes people feel better.'

But she had been glad to travel, tiring of one job and moving on.

'... then I left there and I went up north as housekeeper to Lord and Lady Black. I got fed up with that, so I came back down here. It's nice to go round like that. It's nice to move around.'

It was difficult to persuade her to follow on any questioning about the past or comparisons between past and present society. For instance, once when I asked her how she thought the past compared with the present she changed the subject straight away to talk about her neighbours.

'... oh I don't know. I don't think about it. Have you been in no 10? ...'

Her attitude to present society, however, seemed to be a generally positive one. She thought welfare services were much improved. The workhouse was gone and people received better pensions. Life had been very hard in the past.

Miss Norman liked to talk most about things around her. Her morale was high. She said she missed working a little, but generally enjoyed life. She gossiped a lot about life in the housing scheme and seemed rather too inquisitive about other people's affairs. Other people in the scheme saw her and her sister as busybodies and lived in some apprehension of them. She took an interest in politics and read the newspaper and watched television. But her main passion was small-scale gambling, both on horse racing and football pools. The most exciting times in the week were waiting for the results.

My general impression of Miss Norman was of a very active, indeed almost hyperactive lady. Though curious about other people, she was shy about herself. Her movements were surprisingly quick, and her sudden appearances outside doors and upstairs disturbed a number of the other residents. She also had some seemingly paranoid ideas about other people in the flats and the man in the next house who she thought was spying on her. It was interesting that her sister seemed to share the same thoughts and behaviour. Some of the other tenants were clearly afraid of them. For Miss Norman, the fault, if there was one, lay with the other people.

'... they are jealous you know, because there's two of us, you see, and they don't like it. There's a lot of people you can't get on with, you know, a lot of people ...'

She did befriend some of her frailer neighbours, however, and took particular trouble to visit one old lady who was in hospital quite a distance away and had become completely blind.

I saw Miss Norman intermittently through the 1970s. She remained fit, walking out a lot with her sister. Her conversation centred about events in the house. She hardly ever spoke about events in the past. In the course of 1981 I spoke with her three times, when she was 79 years old. A couple of years previously she had been moved to a modern sheltered housing scheme, one hundred yards away from the old one. Her sister had also been moved to another scheme at a greater distance. (According to the warden they had been causing 'trouble' and it was thought better to separate them.) Miss Norman said she was fit and well. But recently she had developed pains in the arms and found she could not bend. The doctor had diagnosed angina of the heart. Her room was exceptionally hot, with an extra electric fire on, as she said she felt the cold easily. Her hearing was worse, as I could observe, and she said she did not go to church anymore because she could not hear.

In many ways, however, her behaviour was similar to ten years previously. Her contacts had remained the same. She saw her sister every day, and also regularly saw other friends and relatives. She 'spoke to everybody, even babies in their prams'. She liked to help other people and had 'an open door'. But her 'paranoid' ideas had become somewhat more extreme. She thought that there was a man speaking to her through her hearing aid. He often said 'crazy' things to her, but at the same time was interested in her welfare. He wanted to know where she was going when she went out and would look after her, picking her up if she fell, although she never saw him. She also thought that her neighbours next door were spying on her through the wall. This was possible, she said, because the cement was crumbling, having been wrongly set in the first place.

Her attitude to her past life had become somewhat more positive. To the same questions I had asked ten years before she answered that she had been lucky, 'never having been ill before' in her life. In all lives there were some mistakes. She had got the important things and was well satisfied. She was glad she had not married as it would have brought 'too much trouble'. As ten years previously, she said she did not think about the past, nor did she talk about it. It had no point. But she said that her memories were good ones. She said she remembered especially her childhood, taking the papers out for her father, but she was much more interested in what she was going to do tomorrow than what she did in the past.

Despite the evident discomfort caused by her heart condition, her morale was very high, which she attributed to her 'happy nature'. She was interested in a number of things, horse racing (she said she had won a lot of money), football pools and newspaper competitions, and she enjoyed talking about them. She gave me one football pools form to fill in for myself and pressed me to send it in (it did not win!). However, she admitted that the recent pain that she was suffering meant that she was not able to do housework as she used to, and this sometimes exasperated her, for example, when she had the floor to wash and could not do it. Shopping also was difficult because her arms were 'heavy'. But these difficulties did not disturb her basic frame of mind. She believed in God and said she had no fear of death at all, although she appeared agnostic about prospects for a life to follow.

She maintained the same tolerant attitudes to society that she had expressed previously. People exaggerated things, she said. Crime had not got worse. Young people were the same they had always been. She was not pessimistic about prospects for nuclear war. She was sure people would unite to stop it. She saw a lot of young people going to churches now. Before I left she pressed into my hand a copy of 'Awake!', a publication of the Jehovah's Witnesses. Soon after this last visit, Miss Norman's physical condition deteriorated quickly. She fell a number of times, and did not eat properly. At the beginning of 1982 she was admitted to hospital and discharged to her sister's flat but died a few days later.

As far as I could observe there was considerable continuity in Miss Norman's life between 1971 and 1981. A high degree of interest in present activities, a lack of involvement in the past, and a high level of morale. Just prior to 1981 her health had begun to deteriorate but Miss Norman had not let this disturb her equanimity. She tried to maintain as high a level of activity as she could, and perhaps as a result, died soon afterwards. She denied any sense of change in her own personality. 'I'm just the same as I was when I was younger.' A disturbing feature of her personality were her paranoid ideas which had remained with her also over the ten years, albeit in different forms. They were well known to others and apparently shared by her sister—a case of *folie à deux* perhaps? It should be noted however, that they did not make her unhappy, rather they served to make life more interesting for her, if not for others!

Miss Norman's case demonstrates little about the function of reminiscence, except to illustrate again someone who felt no need to dwell on the past. What she was about to do today or tomorrow was of sufficient interest to hold her attention, and this was true of her in her late seventies as well as late sixties. However, it is interesting to note how in her case as well as in others in this study (for example, Mr Currie in Chapter 6) maintenance of good health during old age appeared to be a factor which had led to an increase in expressed satisfaction with past life. Maintaining good health until an advanced age seems to produce a sense of 'good fortune', perhaps especially as a result of comparisons with contemporaries who are not so lucky.

Subsequent History of Other Cases

It has not been claimed that those people who did not reminisce and saw no point or purpose in it formed a coherent group. What they shared in common was a lack of concern with reminiscence, denial of its importance to themselves, and a belief that there were other and better ways of coping with life in old age. In Chapter 5 it was concluded that a positive, valuing attitude to personal memories seemed indicative of subsequent successful psychological adjustment to the stresses of late life. Can the same be said of a dismissive attitude? The answer seems to be yes. Of the 15 people with such an attitude to reminiscence, one, Mr Sapper, who had very much disliked his life circumstances, moved out of the housing complex a couple of years before I next visited, and I was unable to trace him. But of the remaining 14, possibly as many as 12 and certainly 11 people seemed to maintain a high degree of morale until their deaths. Furthermore, the stability in the attitudes they expressed, including attitudes to reminiscence, was one of the most striking features of this longitudinal study.

The three people who had reminisced a lot on my first encounter with them, but then spoke no more about the past, were all very old and died within a short time after the completion of my initial visits. Mr Wickens died one year later after a fall. I saw him a few months before he died. He had not been able to go outside for a long while because of arthritis in his feet, but he was still cheerful and very much in control of his situation. At the time I called he was busy cooking. He wished me well and gave me a detailed list of the times in the week when it was convenient for him to talk with me. Regarded as the 'father' of the housing scheme, he was greatly missed after his death.

Mrs Williams died within two years, and I did not see her again. According to the warden, she became more complaining in her last years. This he found sad because she had been so brave before in facing her considerable difficulties without complaint. Certainly, her situation was a very difficult one. She was almost totally blind and capable of little movement. Also she lived in a block on the other side of the road from the rest of the sheltered housing scheme and had few visitors. Mrs Stanton I saw once, not long before she left the housing scheme to go to live with her son. She spoke about her quiet pleasures in life—reading and praying. She died three years later and was said by the warden to have remained happy. Mrs Stanton had told me on a previous occasion that she did sometimes feel a little lonely in the evening, although it was nothing to complain of. Going to church on Sunday with her son's family was the highlight of her week. She welcomed the invitation to live with them.

Those who were dissatisfied with their lives, both past and present, remained dissatisfied. As already mentioned, I did not follow up Mr Sapper after he left the housing scheme. Mrs Ball died within a year and became increasingly depressed. Unable to go out much—she had two nasty falls in her last year—she wished she had never left her old neighbourhood. Mr Charles also died within the year and was apparently depressed beforehand. The warden described him as not looking after himself well in his last year.

All the people who expressed positive attitudes to their lives seemed to continue to cope remarkably well, just as Mrs Faith, Mr Lothian and Miss Norman did. Mr Butcher died suddenly of a heart attack in the following year, as did Mrs Ditton. Mrs Topps lived a further five years to the age of 93. She became depressed initially in the period in which she was housebound following a fall, but after she began going out again she fully recovered. When I last saw her she said she 'enjoyed what she could' and was disappointed but not depressed anymore in the weeks when she could not be taken to the old people's club. She spoke openly of her need for visitors and company, and seemed quite successful in securing them. She grumbled pleasantly at me for visiting so little! She had always put such a high value on keeping active and involved, and all things considered she was remarkably successful in remaining active up to such an advanced age. She was spoken of with admiration by people in the housing scheme before and after she died.

Mrs Emery on the other hand voluntarily and somewhat surprisingly gave up the struggle to remain living in sheltered housing, and moved into a residential care home. She was not under pressure from the warden to do this. According to all accounts I received she remained happy and had high morale in the home as well, keeping up her appetite for books and receiving regular visits from her friends. The home was also in the same neighbourhood where she had lived. She died four years after admission.

Of the other women besides Mrs Faith whom old age had given new opportunities, Mrs Taylor lived another eight years and Mrs Tooley another seven years until the ages of 94 and 81 respectively. The similarities between all three women remained. All maintained their hobbies, their rooms and their general appearance very well, and they spoke positively of old age despite the difficulties they incurred. Mrs Taylor developed cataracts in her eyes which for a period prevented her from reading or sewing as she used to. She complained of the boredom, but looked forward to the operation, and still took a lot of pleasure in her room and her furnishings. Two years later, at the age of 90, she had shingles badly, but again recovered well and expressed positive attitudes when I visited her a few months afterwards. In the last year of her life she went to live in an old people's home but I was not able to visit or hear about her there. Mrs Tooley developed arthritis badly in both legs and hands and gradually became housebound. Still she did not become noticeably depressed. She appreciated visits from her daughter and her son, but also appreciated the independence she still had, which had perhaps been missing in her earlier life. 'Why ever did you get married?' she asked me when we last met, and the question—surprising in context—was probably revealing of her own attitude to marriage. All three women were easy going, and seemed happy as long as their independence was not threatened.

None of these three seemed to change in their attitudes to reminiscence. The past never seemed to feature in their later conversations with me, nor in any of the other people described in this chapter. This constancy of attitude makes it natural to think of the members of this group as quite distinct from the reminiscers discussed in Chapter 5, whose orientation to reminiscence also remained constant.

Wherein this difference lies is open to speculation. Insufficient evidence was collected using the 16PF personality questionnaire, to seek relationships with other individual characteristics. It would seem plausible to look for systematic differences as well in their life history experiences. As far as actual expression of satisfaction with past life is concerned, however, there was little if any difference between the two groups, but the reminiscers clearly viewed their memories as more vital, pleasurable and meaningful. It seems best to try to understand this capacity to enjoy the past in its own terms, and derive clues as to its origin and development from writers who have explored their own need to reminisce, as Salaman (1970). In the context of this study, however, it needs to be asserted that reminiscence is certainly not the only means of coping in old age. The path of the non-reminiscer who has found or maintains other ways of coping seems equally valid, and, what is more, equally feasible.

Chapter 8

Loss and Depression

Distinguishing Characteristics

The last and smallest of the groups whose attitudes to reminiscence I distinguished were those who also did not like to reminisce, but who at the same time expressed a distinct uneasiness about thinking on the past. In this they resembled more the compulsive reminiscers of Chapter 6. The latter reminisced, although they wished they did not, whereas these non-reminiscers had to avoid reminiscence although their memories in themselves were predominantly pleasant.

Mr Cox had run away from home at the age of 14 and gone to sea. His father was a station master and had been 'too severe, too religious'. Mr Cox had never seen or 'wanted to see' his parents again. But he had had a 'wonderful life' as a cook on board ships and had later had a very happy marriage. He and his wife had lost their only children, twin sons who died together in a boat torpedoed in the Second World War. The last part of his life had been dedicated to his wife until she died two years before I met him. The warden confirmed how devoted a couple they had been. Now at the age of 83 he saw no point in living. He had made two suicide attempts and the warden felt she had to be very careful with him. She characterized him as having a 'chip on his shoulder'. She had recently got him to go to the pub with another tenant. He walked with the aid of sticks as he had arthritis in both legs.

When I spoke to him he told me that his greatest wish was to die, and he expressed a lot of anger towards his doctor for not being understanding and doing nothing to help him to die. He said he would like to see a 'euthanasia bill' passed. He spoke proudly of his past life—he showed me his ship passage book—and of his wife. But now he felt useless, with no-one to look after or to cook for—his wife had always let him do the cooking when he was at home. He regretted, too, having to move from his old house on a council compulsory order. He poured scorn on the state of the country—it was a 'muck heap, not England any more'. There was no point in living. He said he sat in his seat all day with only the television for company.

Because he spoke so enthusiastically about his past, I encouraged him on the first occasion I visited him to tell me about his various experiences. This he did, but more I felt to oblige me than because it was what he wanted to do. He said he did reminisce to some extent, but that it was no help at all to him. It was such a contrast with the misery of his present. There was no way, he said, his situation could be improved. He wanted to 'get out of it'.

Despite his anger with his situation and his suspicion once that I had something to do with the housing department (with whom he was very angry because of a rent increase), he was always very willing to help me with any questions and thanked me for coming. He died quite suddenly at the end of the year, following a heart attack after a bout of pneumonia from which he had at first seemed to recover.

Mr Bungay by contrast was not a friendly man. The first time I called he remained standing all the time. Rather curt and humourless, he was not popular with the warden and the other tenants, who saw him as a 'born grumbler'. Gradually, however, he came to accept me, although he said he did not expect I would understand his feelings. His life too had revolved to a great extent around his relationship with his wife. He had worked for 46 years for the London Underground, but apart from that he had spent nearly all his time at home with his wife. He described himself as a 'stick in the mud'. He and his wife had very seldom gone out. She had died six years previously and the time since then seemed like 'ages'. Like Mr Cox, he idealized his wife—she was 'an ideal woman'—and said he could not expect to be happy without her. He was only sustained, he said, by his religious belief that they would meet again in the life beyond. He said he was very satisfied with his past life. But he would not talk about the past and was quite clear in his attitude in this regard. He tried not to reminisce—he said he 'held it in check'—because the comparison with the present was too depressing. It was certainly no help. Thinking about the past 'did not pay'. It made him 'descend into the depths' of depression.

The major part of his conversation, indeed, consisted in various complaints about the welfare services and the council. There was no adequate bus service—the scheme where he lived was situated a long way from any shops. He had also written to the housing manager to complain about a recent increase in the rates and was annoyed that he had received no proper reply. His morale was very low and he exhibited some symptoms of depression, saying he felt useless and was not able to enjoy things anymore. He received little sympathy from people and he said he did not expect it. In the housing scheme it was like 'living in a world of one's own'. He spoke very little about his two daughters, one of whom he saw once a week. Their relationship, he said, was quite all right as it was. They did not want him hanging around them. He did not want them to be hanging around him.

Mr Jewell was the third man in the group to express similarly negative attitudes to reminiscing, and like Mr Cox and Mr Bungay had recently been bereaved and had not come to terms with living alone. He wanted to find another 'companion'. His case is described in detail later on in this chapter.

The three women in this group, by contrast, had been widowed further back in their lives. They had suffered other recent losses, though, which had severely disturbed them. Mrs Jackson's life had been suddenly changed by a stroke in 1969 which had badly affected both her legs and arms and meant she could not go out on her own. Her speech had also been affected for a time but had now recovered. Although by then already 77 years old, she had remained active in voluntary welfare work up until the time of her stroke. Her husband had died ten years previously and her one son and two daughters lived in other parts of the country.

Now she felt very depressed and this itself worried her more, she said, because it was 'not her nature to be depressed'. She hated to complain, she said. People thought she was a 'hypochondriac' because she looked much better than she was, she said, and this hurt her very much. She felt useless and missed going out shopping. She wished now that her family was not so far away and she regretted moving to the housing scheme after the stroke, because it was so far away from her old neighbourhood and all her old friends. She was eager to help me, but obviously embarrassed by her disabilities, her shaking legs in particular.

She was satisfied with her past life, she said, and she spoke proudly in particular of her early experiences in life. Her father had died when she was 13, and at 16 she had left home to become a companion to the Swedish consul's daughter in London. Life had been very interesting for her then. But she was definite that she did not like to reminisce, that it worried her and made it harder for her to adjust to her present situation.

Mrs Tucker's case is also described later in this chapter. Like Mrs Jackson, she had only a couple of years previously had a major change in her way of life. Up to then she had always lived within close family relationships. After her husband died, she had lived first with her daughter and then with her son. Now having to come to live alone in a sheltered housing scheme, she found it difficult to cope. She was disoriented. She also did not like to reminisce.

Mrs Kitchen was the one person in this group of people that said that reminiscing made them sad and was therefore best avoided, who seemed to have reasonably high morale when I first met her in 1971. Like a number of the other women in my sample, she had been in service (which included a period with the writer Arnold Bennett) and did not regret it at all. She was a strong royalist (a portrait of the Queen hung in her room) and she also supported the existence of an aristocracy because they 'acted as benefactors' to the rest of the population. Although initially suspicious about the purpose of my research, she became kindly and affectionate and liked offering me tea from a fine tea service. I could also observe that she had a number of other regular visitors, including her sister and an old friend, who were sometimes there when I called.

Her negative attitude to reminiscing was the more surprising because she made many comments on how life in England generally had changed for the worse. Her room also contained a number of old family photographs. She spoke of a happy marriage with her husband, who had died six years previously.

A clue as to what was wrong came when I wanted to fill in my questionnaire on social contacts. She was defensive about answering questions about her only daughter who lived outside London. She asked me to write down that she saw her 'as much' as before, and even wanted to check that I had written that down. Later on I discovered from the warden that her daughter 'neglected' her but he did not know why. This made her sad, he said, and explained why she emphasized instead her memories of her loving husband (in fact to me she did not speak a great deal about her husband although she did stress how good he had been).

I spoke to her in all on six occasions in 1970 and 1971. She indicated no marked symptoms of depression, either on the MMPI depression scale, the Life Satisfaction Index or in general conversation. Indeed, she expressed a great deal of satisfaction with her life. A lot of her conversation was devoted to the state of the world and political issues, crime, unions and the Irish problem, for example. This was quite unusual for the women in this sample, who tended to speak much more about family matters. She was emphatic that she did not like to reminisce. It made her 'sad'. She said it was important not to 'brood on past memories' but to 'keep up an interest in the present'.

Although ostensibly well adjusted I did write in my notes at the time that she showed signs of a 'sad nervous tension'. She also made a puzzling remark about herself which she repeated twice on different occasions, that I 'should not put a halo' over her. She said that she had said the same 'to relatives'.

All of these six people who expressed similar attitudes to reminiscence, namely an avoidance of thinking about the past, despite its happiness, and usually precisely because of its happiness, had suffered serious losses which they had not been able to come to terms with. Mr Cox, Mr Bungay and Mr Jewell had all been recently bereaved and could not bear living alone. Mr Cox wanted to die. Mr Bungay's only solace was his belief in a life to come where he would meet his wife again. Mr Jewell wanted to find another wife.

Bereavement was not the issue with the three women, but they had suffered other forms of loss which caused them great pain. Mrs Jackson had lost her old active way of life, as the result of one sudden stroke that had made her housebound. And at the same time she had moved to a sheltered housing scheme far away from her old neighbourhood and friends. Mrs Tucker lamented the loss of her old family oriented life. She did not feel 'right' living alone after the years she had lived in a close family network. Mrs Kitchen was the one person who, at first appearance, did not appear to fit the same pattern. But there was an underlying sorrow in her life concerning a rift with her daughter which she did not like to admit to.

The cases of Mr Jewell and Mrs Tucker which follow, illustrate how incapacitating the impact of loss can be, and also how often the symptoms of depression are not picked up by the health and welfare agencies. Both, however, presented, as Mr Jewell himself said, 'social problems'. Medication may have benefited them, but a more supportive psychotherapeutic or social work intervention was needed as well to help them grapple with the underlying issues. Both were searching for substitutes for what they had lost, Mr Jewell for a new wife, Mrs Tucker for renewed close links with her family.

Of course, loss is a particularly common experience in old age, and most people cope remarkably well. Were the losses that these people suffered qualitatively or quantitatively worse than others already mentioned in this book? That is a difficult question to answer. For some the experience of loss in old age appeared to reactivate earlier losses that perhaps had never been fully absorbed before. Mrs Tucker, as will be evident, when she did reminisce spoke mainly about earlier losses to her family. Mr Cox had lost his two sons in the war. When his wife died he experienced himself as completely alone. Others, however, attributed their depression partially to the protective environment they had lived in earlier in life. Mr Jewell for example spoke of how his parents had not allowed him to 'rough it' as a child and a young man. He had had to learn later what hardship was. Certainly a 'lifestyle' approach to understanding coping with loss, such as described by Williams and Wirths (1965), brings into sharp focus why a number of these people experienced such a discontinuity in their lives. Mrs Tucker had been all her life essentially a 'family' person, Mrs Jackson a 'community' person. Mr Bungay had not had, and never wanted to have, a life outside working and being at home with his wife. Mr Cox had cut off his links with his family as a young man and had devoted all his attention in his later life to his wife.

As to their disinclination to reminisce, essentially the same phenomenon has been reported in other studies. McMahon and Rhudick described how the depressed subjects in their sample showed the greatest difficulty in reminiscing (McMahon and Rhudick, 1964). Kaminsky argues that in severe depression the memory of well being is 'so decathected, it temporarily disappears, and depressed persons suffer from the illusion of always having been depressed'. Thus, the only memories available are those which exacerbate and enlarge on the themes of present pain; 'memory serves as another grand inquisitor which accuses the suffering person the incapacities whose loss he laments' (Kaminsky, 1984, p.154). This description certainly fits the selective, sad recall of Mrs Tucker, recounting the history of losses within her family.

A key point to me though seems to be another one raised by McMahon and Rhudick where they speculate that the absence of reminiscence in depressed people may be related to the absence of mourning during the 'interrupted grief reaction' (McMahon and Rhudick, 1964). The analogy between reminiscence and grieving is a strong one, and has also been made more recently by Pollack (1981) and Castelnuovo-Tedesco (1980). Like the work of mourning, reminiscence involves a reorganization of the relationship to the lost other. Reminiscence too can involve obsessive recounting. It can appear to reflect self absorption. It can result in a failure to give up what has been lost. Indeed for those who never give up wishing for a return to the past, reminiscence may not be pleasurable because they are unable to detach themselves from, and freely enjoy their memories of the past as memories. This seemed to be a common feature of the people in this group.

The link between inhibited reminiscence and grief reactions, and the implications for those working with older people will be discussed further in Chapter 10.

Mr Jewell

Mr Jewell was a quietly spoken man of 72, of short build. He was pleased to help
me with my research, and even volunteered, through me, to be tested in another
project being carried out at London University at the same time on the cognitive
functioning and memory of older people. He stressed that I could ask him any
questions I wanted, and write down what I thought.

'... if you have any notes to write down on your foolscap when you get home, you're
welcome.'

Although not shy in expressing his views, for example on modern society, he
tired of speaking for too long a time at one go, and our conversations never
lasted more than an hour. But he was always pleased to see me again. I visited
him in all eight times in the course of 1971.

He had been born into a Jewish family in the East End of London in 1899. He
remembered a happy childhood.

'... I had a very good childhood, I had very good parents. They never demanded
anything of me. My father had a grocer's shop in the East End for about 35 years and we
never wanted for anything as youngsters. A lot of the population of them days in the East
End, half the year the parents were out of work. It was the industries they were in. But as
far as my finances were concerned, we weren't short of anything. We had plenty of food,
holidays—good food naturally, because my parents were in the trade. So I had a good
childhood.'

His parents had been fairly easy going with him.

'... I don't know if it was any good to me, but they weren't strict, not in my estimation,
they weren't strict.'

When he left school at 14 his parents encouraged him to go into the fur trade,
as a number of his other relatives were furriers. For two years he worked in the
city and then for the rest of his career worked in the West End of London,
moving from firm to firm but always staying in the same area. A number of
times he was out of work, but he could always rely on his parents.

'... I was always in the fur trade. I didn't know anything else. So actually when I was out
of work at any time, it was difficult to pick up another job because I didn't know anything
else ... When I was out of work the only thing was I had good parents, I always had my
bed. Always had my food. I wasn't short of anything. Even if I wasn't working, I knew I
had a regular meal. My parents didn't depend on my pound or two a week.'

He was called up for the army at the age of 18 in 1917, but was rejected as
unfit, probably on account of his height. Later on he married a Jewish girl and
he described his married life as a happy and united one. He had one son. His
work career, however, was not as successful as he would have wished. Twice he
was in business on his own, but he let opportunities slip by. Partly this seemed to

be his fault as he failed to take initiatives, but he was also unlucky in his choice of business partners.

'... it hasn't made me rich. I had the opportunities. I don't know if I would say I was slow or just let them slip by me. I was a "guvnor" twice on my own but I had partners, both times, and they were both wrong partners and they discouraged me. What I should have done is taken the bull by the horns, kept on my own and finished my partners, but I didn't see things in that light at the time, because I was so discouraged. I was established in the West End and all. One was a non-worker and one was a bit of a twister. One would come in about ten o'clock in the morning and want to go early and all that. But if you're partners, you've got to be working partners, and work together ... I was unlucky. I picked the wrong partners, or wrong partners picked me.'

He had been for a period involved in politics with the local Labour Party, but became disillusioned by what he saw.

'...it's quite a big racket on the inside, it's like professional people, doctors, barristers, architects, I call them one band of bandits. They are all in with one another, they are only out for what they can get ... once they get into politics it's like a manager or a foreman, once he's in the job he looks after it. He's got to be a "guvnor's" man. If they're going to look on the man on the street's side all of the time, they'd never keep their job. I was never a "yes" man. Inside politics unless you're a "yes" man you'll never get anywhere.'

His latter years had been made difficult by his wife's poor health. She came to suffer from bad circulation of the blood and was a 'semi-invalid' from 1959. She became depressed and in 1965 had a 'nervous breakdown' and remained in a psychiatric hospital for six months. It was at that time that Mr Jewell decided that it would be better for them to move into sheltered housing. The consultant psychiatrist encouraged him to retire to be with his wife.

'... "Put in for your pension, retire and be with your wife and she'll get her confidence back much quicker. She needs somebody with her all day." So what I done, I retired. She used to do the light chores and a bit of cooking. I used to do the main errands and the clearing up. Eventually she was all right, but if I was out anywhere a bit too long, when I came back she was very quiet. While I was with her she was OK.'

They liked living in the sheltered housing scheme very much and they furnished their apartment well. But his wife's circulation problems became worse, her big toe had to be amputated because of gangrene, and when she died in 1969 it was, he said, 'a happy release'.

It was only two years after his wife's death that I first spoke to him, and he complained greatly of loneliness.

'... I'm not used to being alone. Well I don't think anyone is who has had a family or married life and loses it. Naturally they can't cope being alone ... a man can less cope than a woman. A woman in the home when she's been married is occupied in the home, whereas the man isn't. But the man when he's on his own, he's got to kind of lead a complete new life, cope with the home, see, even if he's retired like me or not, he's still got to cope with the home when he's left on his own ... a woman copes better than a man, I'm not saying she's not still lonely, but they go to these old friendship clubs, the old people there, there's more women in them than men. A man if he goes, he feels out of place because 90 per cent of these friendship clubs are nearly all women.'

His present morale was low and he admitted to a number of symptoms of depression: feeling low, feeling weak and unwell, feeling unable to get going. He also clearly identified himself as suffering from depression, but expected no help from a doctor as it was a 'social problem', not a medical one. It was because he was alone, and his main hope was to find a woman companion, preferably 20 or 30 years younger than himself.

'... I went to a club with a friend of mine to pick up someone as a companion partner, but they were too old for me, they were 60 to 70. I know I'm that age, but I don't want a woman that age because I feel much younger.'

He seemed to expect a better future for himself and was also thinking of doing some part-time work again in the fur trade.

Reminiscence, he said, he did very little. Thoughts had tended to come back more since his wife died, but he tried to avoid them. He was not dissatisfied with his past life, and he did not wish it had been different. He did say, though, that he did not regard himself as lucky and that he had not got most of the important things in life. As already mentioned, his regrets were mainly over missed opportunities at work. He didn't have the necessary expertise and the ability to make the right judgements.

'... I've looked at things in life too late. I should have looked at things like I'm talking 30 or 40 or 50 years ago. I might have been a rich man today if I had, I don't know.'

But all in all he had a favourable view of himself.

'...I can look in a glass and say, well have I been too stern or been to easy? Have I done right, have I done wrong? I ask myself that and I think I've taken the middle course. That means I've not been too hard and I've not been too easy ...'

His memories, both of childhood and married life, were pleasant ones. He said he had almost no unpleasant ones. Yet he did not like to reminisce. Rather than cheer him up, looking back, precisely because he had been so happy, made him 'more miserable' and made it harder for him to adjust to present circumstances. On the reminiscence questionnaire he answered that thinking of the past made it harder for him, because 'I wished I had now what I had in the past'. He elaborated on this in his conversation.

'... no, I don't think it does [cheer you up] because you know you had a happy past. You know you had a happy married life. Even though my wife, the last few years of her life, was a bit unfortunate—as I told you she had a bad medical history—we were still good companions, see. I looked after the wife, and as far as the wife could do with the chores, she looked after me. So really I had a happy single life and I had a happy married life. So in the position I am at the moment it's not good to look back. It makes you more miserable than you have to, you see.'

He associated reminiscence with depression.

'... at times I do [think about past life], when I've got the depression coming on, I think back. But otherwise I don't think so often when I haven't got the depressed feeling.'

He was lucky to have his son's family living not far away, and he visited them once or twice a week and took an interest in his two young grandchildren. He visited an old neighbour. His brothers, however, were too far away to visit frequently. What he wanted above all was another companion to replace his first wife.

'... they finished [decorating] the flat about two weeks before Christmas. I said the only thing it's short of is a woman in the place.'

His views on modern society were remarkably favourable. He remembered how bad housing had been.

'... the housing is much better because of the bombing of London during the war. It could be, if all these old buildings hadn't been flattened in all these cities, it could be that they would still be standing up and people living in them. There wouldn't be these nice council blocks like there are now. As far as that's concerned, Hitler done a good thing to flatten some of these places, barring the people that got injured and killed ... I know I used to work in the City as a youngster. If you were in a fire in those buildings they were death traps because there was nothing else but wood and little ladders where the fire engine could never get up to ... all the buildings were rat infested and about 100 years old. The bombing did a bit of good as far as the City of London is concerned.'

He liked the young.

'... you hear of these clashes with hippies and that, but to a gang of 50 hippies there are 500 serious minded students that are studying ... I've seen some of the university teams on "University Challenge" on the television and some of them look real hippies and yet they are real serious educated minded students, studying seriously ... yet if you saw them people in the street you would think they were long haired hippies. But they are educated serious minded students, very clever. They are the people that will be ruling our country in the future, and I'm very glad to see it. Let them have long hair, I don't mind. Their long hair doesn't alter their outlook on life. If they've got something there in the back of their mind, they can wear flowers all over their shirts, I don't mind ...'

Old people, he thought, found it hard to adapt.

'... life is much faster now, see, and naturally the older generation can't cope with the speed, they can't, they don't attempt to. Everything is all speeded up, whereas we used to work ten or twelve hours a day in our time, well now it's an eight hour day, sometimes even less.'

He would like to be young again himself in the present.

'... there was a lot to account for that was bad in the old days. The thing is, we old people, to take advantage of the good days now, we should be 20 or 30 years younger. That's the whole thing about it. We're too old really to take advantage. Now it's for the younger generation to have the benefit of it.'

He hoped nevertheless to live to enjoy a better world.

'... I'm hoping still to live a nice few years. If I'm going to be that lucky to live a few years which I hope to, I want to see that improvement, and I want to see the younger people that are going to vote and partly rule the country. It's going to be to my advantage and all, although I'm old and retired. That's why I still look to the future.'

He saw the present problems of the country as relating fundamentally to the strife in industry, the inability of both sides, union and management, to appreciate the need to work together. But he was basically optimistic.

He was proud of his Jewish background. Religion provided principles and that was important—being a 'good Methodist, good Catholic, good Protestant. I'm what I might call a good Jew'.

'... I think it is important to be a little bit on the religious side, because having that at the back of your mind, it gives you a little bit of conscience, doing right or doing wrong, but a person that hasn't got a religion can do wrong and still think they are doing right.'

But he was above all tolerant in this regard as in others.

'... I never like to debate on religion because there's such a lot, you could never end ...'

'... I went to an ordinary council school, I think there must have been about 400 pupils in that school, and there couldn't have been more than about 20 Jewish boys in there. I got on with all of them. In fact, if I got into a fight I'd have many a gentile come up to take my part, if I couldn't take my own part. I will say I'm a good mixer ... well as a matter of fact my son married a gentile girl, she's a very good mother, very good wife, she's a very very good daughter-in-law. We've got no qualms, we let them get on with it and they are very happy together ... that's all my wife and I was concerned about. If she wants the children to become Jewish later on, that's up to her. If she don't, well, she knows we would have liked her to have turned Jewish, ... as long as they are living happy together, that's all I am concerned with.'

The general impression I gained of Mr Jewell in 1971 was of a quiet, helpful and open-minded man. He seemed at first appearance timid, but in fact he was quite self-assured in his views. He was willing to fill in the Cattell 16PF personality questionnaire to help me. From the profile this produced his exceptional qualities appeared to be 'affected by feelings', 'assertive', 'suspicious' and 'apprehensive'. He seemed unhappy inside, which he blamed on his circumstances. He hoped they would change.

At the time of writing, Mr Jewell is still alive and now aged 86, and I have spoken to him on ten occasions in the intervening 14 years. His attitudes have changed very little indeed over these years, as indeed also his general appearance. On each of the three occasions I saw him in the later 1970s, he said he was 'not well' and did not want to speak much. I noted that his appearance was somewhat more untidy than it had been. The warden, however, reported little change, commenting that he went out regularly shopping and rested a lot in his room.

He later told me that he had been greatly affected by his son's divorce in 1977. It had come as a great shock to him and he was glad his wife had not been alive to see it. His son's gambling had been a major cause. He kept in regular contact with his daughter-in-law and grandchildren but had not seen his son since the divorce. When I saw him in 1982 he was hoping for a reconciliation between his son and daughter-in-law. He had recently met them both at the hospital where his grandson had entered for an operation. But in 1985 he recognized that this was not to be. He still saw a lot of his daughter-in-law and his grandchildren and followed their careers with interest. But his son he never saw. He said his son had become embittered after the divorce and taken it out on him. Why, he did not know. He no longer seemed so upset by what must have been a very painful rift with his only son.

Ten years after my first interviews, in the course of 1980–82, I spoke to Mr Jewell on six occasions and covered the same topics as before. His self presentation was almost identical to ten years previously. He said he felt depressed and lonely. Often he was unwell with headaches. His flat had become more untidy, but he showed no sign of mental deterioration. He was as helpful as before and patient in answering questions. A traffic accident in 1978, when he had been hit in the leg by a passing car, had left him with a weakened leg, but in other respects his physical health was good. His main problem was depression, and this was, as he said before, not an 'illness' but a 'social problem' brought about by his being alone.

His attitude to his past life was if anything more positive than before. He no longer regarded himself as unlucky. He had kept good health and he was well satisfied with what he had achieved. He still queried if he had got the important things he wanted in life, but then added 'things just turned out naturally'. He admitted to reminiscing more than he had done ten years previously and put it down to being unhappy and depressed and 'thinking about what might have been'. Again he stressed his happy memories, especially of childhood, 'very good parents' and 'not short of anything'. But it did not give him a good feeling to think back because his memories did not 'balance up' to his present situation.

He expressed the same depressed attitudes to the present that he did in 1971. His life was dreary and boring. He felt tired. Surprisingly perhaps, he still 'hoped and prayed' things would improve. He still thought he had a young appearance for his age and stressed that he did not want to mix with disabled older people. However, when I saw him in 1982 he had begun to attend the luncheon club held within the sheltered housing scheme. In 1981 he thought he would go on holiday again to the south coast—he had not been since his wife died—but he did not go.

It was particularly noticeable that he spoke in the same terms of his search for another partner in 1981 as he had done in 1971. Things, he said, had not worked out. In 1982 he told me that he had tried unsuccessfully to ask for a partner at the old people's luncheon club.

His optimism about modern society had diminished. Old people, he thought, received insufficient help. Unions demanded too high wages. He was also impressed by the increase in anti-social behaviour, football violence in particular.

The last time I saw him in 1985 he looked to me somewhat brighter in appearance, but when I raised the issue of depression, he nodded and indicated that it was still a big problem. His physical health all considered was good. He had been in hospital for three weeks earlier in the year because of a blood clot that developed in his leg and this had been treated successfully. Once a fortnight he caught the bus to do his shopping in the nearest large shopping centre. He had been given a new colour television by the 'welfare' department who also paid for the maintenance, but he did not look at it much. He went to the luncheon club every day and to the bingo on Friday afternoons, but he did not go to the whist or dancing sessions. His dancing days, he said, were over. A lot of the time he dozed in his room.

He said he reminisced quite a lot about the past, but it did not give him a good feeling. The past had been such happy days. His parents had been very good, perhaps 'too good' as they had 'spoiled' him. I asked him what he meant. He said they had protected him from having to 'rough it' and perhaps that was why he found old age so hard. 'But,' he concluded, 'life is a lottery.' One's course is 'fated' and there was nothing one could do about it.

I asked him whether religion meant more or less to him as he was older. He said it did not mean anything now, because his family was gone. Altogether, with his brothers and sisters and the rest of the family, he had enjoyed the Jewish celebrations, but with no family, religion was gone too.

Mr Jewell is a clear example of a man who has not been able to come to terms with the losses he incurred in his later sixties. The major loss was his wife's early death, but one should not discount the importance too of the loss of his work role which preceded it. Financially his means have been very limited since. Subsequently he has had to face the deaths of his brothers and sisters, and the sad break-up of his son's marriage. In 1971 he felt depressed and lonely because he lived alone; 14 years later he felt the same.

His symptoms of depression were not dramatic enough to be seen to require professional help. He was seen by others, the wardens and probably his doctor, to be coping all right—certainly, as he put it himself, to be in very good health for his age. He identified his own problem as a 'social' one, and it may be that he had not taken the right steps to help himself. He had had ideas about what he should do—find a new life, find a job, go on holiday, but nothing had materialized. Certainly I felt he would have benefitted from group therapy if this had been available to him. To have met regularly with people in similar situations, who could offer support and encouragement to one another, might have led him to take more purposeful actions in his life, for example about going on holiday or finding friends. He was open enough about his thoughts and feelings to enter into such a group.

Reminiscence played no important part in his life. The past was at best irrelevant, and at worst only emphasized the emptiness of his present situation. His attitudes in this respect remained essentially the same. But as he became older he found it more difficult to avoid thinking back. At the age of 72, when I first met him, he was firmly future oriented and was hoping for an improvement in his life. These hopes for change remained with him a long time. But at the age of 86 he had become more reconciled to his situation. Like Mr Wickens (in the previous chapter) he stressed the importance of 'fate', that there was nothing one could do to alter one's life course.

Intriguingly, in my last conversation he looked for some explanation of his present unhappiness in his childhood, a theme that he had mentioned in passing 14 years earlier, that his parents had been really too good to him and had not let him experience what hardship was. This is an unusual admission for someone of Mr Jewell's generation. But then a number of his characteristics seem more representative of a younger generation. He had missed the First World War, he maintained a youthful self image for a long time and he had a positive attitude to social change. His case suggests that depression in old age could become an even more common problem as the generations of more self sufficient older people die away.

Mrs Tucker

I visited Mrs Tucker altogether nine times in the course of 1971 when she was 79 years old. She lived on the top floor of an old Victorian building which had been converted for use as a sheltered housing scheme. She complained a lot about the stairs she had to climb to get to her room. She felt her health was not what it should be and she often called out her GP to come and see her. Nevertheless she managed to go out most days to do her shopping and she received a home help for assistance with her housework. Her main problem, she admitted, was separation from her family. She could not come to terms with living alone. She had four children: one daughter lived in Australia, another in a distant part of London, and her two sons lived outside of London. She had a visit from one of her children most weeks, but she missed greatly regular contact with them. She did a lot of writing, and a long drawn out postal strike in 1971 upset her very much.

'... I write to my sister, I write to Australia, I write to my other daughter, and my son in Berkshire. That's four letters a week, and they all answer them back, but this strike is awful, I feel as if I'm in another world without a letter.'

All her life she had lived within a close knit working class family. She expressed much love for all members of her family, past and present. Her father had worked on the building of the London Underground.

'... he helped to build the first tuppenny tube in London. He got the foundation out. He went down 20 feet on sticks, and he was lowered with a rope round his waist. He couldn't write his own name, but he knew everything underground.'

In her young days she had worked as a waitress at a West End hotel for four years. These had been happy days. She had enjoyed the work and the liveliness of Edwardian London. She remembered how sometimes she used to meet her father after work and on one occasion how he had bought her some new boots with fresh golden sovereigns.

'... high button boots, they were. "I'll meet you, I'll meet you Saturday morning" ... high legged boots right up to there. "Take hold of them." Five golden sovereigns. Oh it looked lovely. He said, "Look they're all new ones this morning". That's how they paid him for night work. That was good money.'

But life was never to be as good again. Her father fell at work and seriously injured himself, soon after the outbreak of the First World War.

'... he had an unlucky fall, he fell down one night while on night work—we often wonder if the rum he drank went to his legs and he fell. He had been at it for years and years, then he fell. He fractured his back, he hurt his legs ... he spent six months in Middlesex Hospital, and he said, "There's something odd here, they're moving us all out, there's something going on". They were getting ready for that war!'

The sufferings inflicted by both the world wars on ordinary people like herself weighed heavily on Mrs Tucker's mind. She told many stories of disasters inflicted both on her own and on other families. She saw the wars in a very personal way. She remembered seeing Kaiser Wilhelm II at King Edwards VII's funeral procession.

'... my cousin said, "Coming to see the old King buried?". I said, "Oh no". "Come on," she said, "get up at four o'clock in the morning, we can wait at the station and have a grand view." There we saw the march pass by us. We saw the Kaiser in the funeral procession. With his helmet and his best feathers. His skeleton bones on his hat, and his horse was a great big grey one, and he danced up and down to the old music. He pranced up and down. He had a job to keep this horse in gear, you know. Little Willie, his son, was very weak, little Willie was behind him. A man said, "That's the one who is going to make the next war, that's the one, coming down here".'

Mrs Tucker married just before the beginning of the First World War and her husband went through very 'rough' times. It left him with long lasting injury and inability to earn much. Life had been very hard for their family. The wars had a lot to answer for.

'... I had to take in lodgers, Irish lodgers, I couldn't manage. My husband kept going. Thirty-three bob a week was all he had. He suffered with his head terrible. He was shot right near the brain ... those times were hard, very hard. You think of the good times, the good times before that ever happened, when you had a few bob. One and a half pence for a packet of cigarettes, sixpence a bottle of beer, fourpence for a pint of beer. They robbed you of everything, those wars, didn't they. Robbed you of everything . . .'

She had had to go to the British Legion for help.

'. . .I had to go at one time he went in hospital, I had nothing left, only a pound to go through with four children. The one at work, she brought in a pound, and I went to the British Legion. I was about the only woman with 300 men. "Where's your husband?" I said, "He's in hospital, would you like to 'phone up, he's in there through his head wound. He's got sciatica and he can't walk". Then they gave me five shillings for groceries. Five shillings for a joint. I said, "Excuse me, but I shall want something to cook it with". So they gave me then three shillings for the gas, and I was to come again. I had a cup of hot coffee and some buns. The man said, "Come again, keep coming" . . . he had only got three pound a week pension. When he died they said he should have had four pound a week and a free house. He gave the best years of his life to the army. The Duke of Cornwall's Light Infantry. I used to say to him, "Write and tell them and let them know" . . .'

The Second World War had been even more 'wicked' than the first. Her sister's family had suffered a direct hit from a bomb. A peacock ornament had proved unlucky for her, brought back from Australia by Mrs Tucker's son who was in the Royal Navy throughout the war.

'. . . when he came back he had some silk things for my daughter and some suits for his father and a big peacock thing for me. It was all beaded, "from the Great War to dearest Mum". I didn't like it ever. I've never liked a peacock, but my sister said she liked it. "Unlucky, they are," I said, "I'll throw it away." She said, "Oh I'll have it, I've got no sons. It's a memento of the war". She had a bad accident soon after. She was just going out with her daughter and a bombshell hit them. She was hit in both legs. She was crippled. One daughter, she got the worst. She died. She was 21. Her husband was up the road in the pub . . . he died from shock soon after, I think, he never got over the shock of that girl going.'

Mrs Tucker herself had had a close encounter with a V-1 bomb.

'. . . I was in the big picture palace, the State in Kilburn, and they hit the top of the building. Oh, and the chandeliers shook like that. They said, "Keep still, keep quiet". They got us all to lie flat in the gangways. We all lay flat. There was a little girl crying. She said, "My mummy don't know I'm out, do get me out". I said, "you can't go out" . . . When we got outside, it was a doodlebug, right across the road. A great big thing you never saw, you would never credit it, a great big thing right across the pavement. It was from the butcher's shop to the street, to the picture palace. About 16 feet long. It hit the top of the building, shattered the top of the picture palace, shattered the dome up there . . . there were wardens each side guarding it, huge big thing, great twisted iron, right across the high road. My poor friend and her husband in London Road, they both got killed, she was shot across the road. And a poor little baby in a pram was shot up the tree, and was hanging there. I said, "There's a pram up there" and it was covered in dust, and the baby was crying, but she wasn't hurt . . .'

She remembered the anxious nights hearing the sounds above in the sky and hoping nothing would come down on them. Bad memories of the war, she said, used to come back to her in the night for a long time afterwards, and keep her awake.

Her immediate family had survived the war relatively intact. Her son had been involved in the D-Day landings and 'come back safe'. Mrs Tucker's husband had kept the news of his involvement from her until the last day. She remembered him writing in his letters, 'Once I get home to old Blighty I'm never going in no more wars'. They had been a happy family again. 'We had a nice house and we were all together.' She had taken her own mum to live with her before the war started.

'... my poor mum only had ten shillings at one time, and her room was seven shillings a week, so I said "Well, you've had enough of that, you can come and live with us. You'll have the ten ...".'

But in the years that followed one by one family members were taken from her.

'I had a mother and I had a husband and a brother all gone, and his [her brother's] boy who went right through Burma, he looked a tower of strength, he looked so well and rosy, and he died of thrombosis, 44 ... he followed his father, his father was a road mender, heaving up great big stones and showing the men how to put it down and how to bump it down with a big hammer ... I couldn't get over him going, I could never believe it. He stood nearly six foot and he had rosy cheeks, he looked really fine, outdoor life and plenty of good food ...'

Mrs Tucker had special regrets about both her mother's and husband's death.

'... I'm sorry my mother had to leave home and go away, and I'm sorry I didn't write to the authorities and tell them my husband needed a change, needed a rest. He kept working to the very end, he needed to give up and rest. He wouldn't give up because he wanted that envelope. He had about eleven pounds a week. In the stores, he was. It was very cold there, and I think to myself, I should have written to the authorities and told them he couldn't do it.'

When Mr Tucker died in 1956, Mrs Tucker went to live for a time with one of her daughters. She then moved to stay with her son (who had been in the navy) after his wife left him, and stayed with him four years helping him with the household and the care of his four children. But when he took the opportunity his work gave him to move to Norfolk, Mrs Tucker preferred to stay in London. By then her daughter's son had taken over the room Mrs Tucker had lived in before, and there seemed no other option but for her to live alone. It was then that she came to the sheltered housing scheme where I met her. She found it very hard to be alone.

'... sometimes I think to myself, "What am I here for? I should be with my family, I shouldn't be here". I go to talk to somebody in the night. "I'd better get up and make a cup of tea for somebody," but there's nobody there. Oh, I shan't be able to stay here another winter. Too lonely. Weekends are so lonely. Don't hardly hear a soul, only one old lady up there. She knocks at the door sometimes, and you meet her in the hall. I said to my daughter, "I'll never be able to stick another winter here". And these hills, and these stairs ...'

She thought about going to Australia, to join her other daughter.

'... I wish I had gone to Austalia when Mr Tucker died and they wanted us out of the house. They gave us 100 pound. I said, "Now's the chance to go" but I was too weak. My leg being crippled you see, I wouldn't have been passed. They won't have weak people in Australia...'

Her concern for her health seemed exaggerated and neither the warden nor the GP appeared to take it seriously. Still they sympathized and humoured her. Whenever she called the doctor to come to see her—which was quite often, in some periods once a week—he usually came to see her. In retrospect though, it would seem to me that her concern about her health should have been taken more seriously as a symptom of depression. Her mood was low. On the MMPID scale she said she often felt depressed, could not sleep well, felt incapable and useless, and had difficulty getting going. She was not able to concentrate, felt unwell and weak all over. She neglected herself, and her room was very cluttered and untidy. It may have always been so, but she said that housework was too much for her, she did not want to be bothered. Perhaps her depression was recognized. Perhaps it was thought that there was nothing medically that could be done. The one bright spot in her life was the old people's day centre down the road which she went to for lunch every day. She looked forward to this, and enjoyed the company.

In fact a great deal of Mrs Tucker's conversation revolved round people she had met at the club, as well as news about her family. She spoke about the past sometimes, but usually more about the present. Her attitude to the past was not always consistent. On the questionnaire she said she thought 'very little' about the past. She said that when she did reminisce it gave her sad feelings and made it harder to bear the life she had. Yet on other occasions she said she thought a lot about the past. Clearly though it was not a pleasant activity for her, and she qualified such statements—'I live in the past, I'm sorry to say ...' She said she thought of the 'dead ones who were gone and should have been saved'.

Quite unlike Miss Martin in Chapter 6, she did not doubt the worthwhileness of her life. She had got the most important things in life, 'good children' in particular. She had some regrets—she wished she had saved money to buy a house of her own—but generally did not criticize herself or any of her family members. Yet she was unable to make reminiscence work for her. She denied that thinking back helped her to gain a greater appreciation of her life. Uppermost in her mind when she did think back was the misfortune her family had suffered. Her memories were dominated by unpleasant events, illnesses, bad housing, bombs and death. Sometimes she personified her experience of loss. Death was a thief. 'They robbed you of everything, those wars.'

Although she did have many happy things to think back on, her young days especially, and various family events throughout her life, she consistently said that reminiscing, whether of good or bad events, made it harder for her to bear her current life. Indeed memories of good things about the past seemed to bring home further to her feelings about what had been lost. The sense of community, for example.

'... yes we were happy, more content, and if you needed a person to come in if you were ill, they came in, as where now, you'd have to pay. Nobody will do anything for you. A little boy who used to live next door to me, I said, "Would you fetch me a loaf, Bobby?". He said, "No, I don't go for my mother, I don't see why I should go for you". Oh, I thought, fancy that, and I went and rang the ambulance to let him be born ... how things have changed. Now a child of long ago—"I'll go, I'll go for you, I'll fetch the bread, some butter. I can get anything at the shop at the top of the road. And if you can't manage a penny I don't mind." How different you see. A child of long ago, a child of the past ...'

Change in society worried and threatened her. The change to decimal coinage upset her in particular and she spoke a lot to me about it—of dealings with the milkman for example. Mr Lothian (Chapter 7) had been well on top of the situation, but Mrs Tucker was not.

'... he's tried to tell me this morning, fivepence halfpenny or one and six. I don't know how I can catch on. Really, we don't know where we are. Why don't they leave well alone. Changing our money after all these years, years and years.'

Despite the negative picture she presented of her current situation, she had hopes for improvements, in particular to have closer contacts with her children again. Clearly, too, she enjoyed her contacts with the other old people, and looked forward to group outings at the day centre. Indeed one of her strengths was a genuine concern for others. She did not only think about her own problems, but had a lively interest in those of other people around her. She was kind hearted. Glimpses of her kindness came through her reminiscences. One Christmas she had saved up and managed to get a big turkey for the family and one for her neighbour too.

'... upstairs there was a woman with six children. I said, "Want a turkey?". "I wouldn't know how to cook it." I said, "I'll show you how to cook it and stuff it". She had one, and a pound of sausages. "Wasn't it beautiful," she said. Her husband came down. He bought me a whisky ...'

I only saw Mrs Tucker on one further brief occasion in the course of the 1970s. She was usually out at the day centre when I called. However, I did hear a lot about her from others in the housing scheme, that she was still the same, complaining a lot about her health and the steps she had to climb, and ringing up her doctor regularly with complaints of pain but apparently no serious medical problems. Her family continued to visit regularly. In 1976 she agreed to go into an old people's home for a short stay but did not like it and after a few days walked all the way back to the sheltered housing scheme!

During 1980 and 1981 when she was 89 years old I did speak to her at length on four occasions. The first time, it had been four years since I had seen her, and she seemed much thinner than before. She also seemed very agitated. Her room had been untidy before, but now she herself looked dishevelled—her clothes not matching. There was a smell of incontinence in the room. She did not remember me at first, although later said she did. She had a lot to say, as before—about her doctor, the hospital, the home help, the pains in her leg, the furniture that she said had been damaged. She spoke about her daughter's family in London, about the death of one of the other tenants. She also spoke a lot quite spontaneously about her mother, and how proud she was of her.

I spoke afterwards to the warden and her deputy. They said that Mrs Tucker had a few months before suffered a mild stroke, and now did a number of 'silly' things, as wandering out in her night clothes. She did not eat properly, nor did she go out shopping anymore. They both were of the opinion that Mrs Tucker should not be in sheltered housing. Indeed the deputy was strongly critical both of the geriatric department at the local hospital which had discharged her after her stroke, and her family, who said they would look after Mrs Tucker, but 'did not do anything'. As she lived in a room on the top floor she could easily fall down the stairs, as one person already had. Ideally, they thought, she should be in a 'psychogeriatric' department. Mrs Tucker, they said, was paranoid and could be violent. A case conference had been organized about her at the local hospital and the home help had spoken up on her behalf, saying that Mrs Tucker had improved after coming home, but 'who was she to know?'. 'They', the wardens, really knew Mrs Tucker better. While we were speaking Mrs Tucker happened to come walking down the stairs. 'What are you laughing at?' she said to the warden, and retreated back up the stairs. 'There you are,' the warden said, to indicate this was an example of her paranoid behaviour. Maybe it was, but it was also a very understandable reaction. I left with the feeling that Mrs Tucker would not be able to remain living in such a setting if the attitudes of the wardens were basically unsympathetic. But in a different type of scheme, perhaps one of the very sheltered housing complexes already developed at that time in other areas of the country, she would be better tolerated.

In fact five months later she was moved to the nearby residential care home run by the local authority social services department. According to the warden's description, she became more confused, threw clothes over the balcony of the staircase, and went out with too little on. The warden's criticisms were directed against the family. Mrs Tucker had been 'a good mother' but the family 'did not want to know'. The implication was clear that she thought Mrs Tucker should have been taken to live with one of her children.

In the old people's home I was able to speak with Mrs Tucker at length one afternoon six months after her admission. She was much more relaxed than before. According to the officer in charge, she had settled down well. She was pleased to see me and talked in her characteristic way about the various people who lived there, as well as about her circumstances beforehand, and how her family was faring. As before, she emphasized her own health problems, in particular her bad legs. But she also expressed great amazement and sympathy at the disabilities of the people she saw around her. She said she was glad to be away from where she was. She accused the warden of having taken her pension money. When I asked her whether she thought a lot about the past, she said she did, and she spoke positively about the good life she had had. A member of the care staff came to call her to tea at 4.15 and she asked me to call again.

Three months later, when I next called her situation was very different. She had been placed in a room along with seven other women, all of whom were mentally impaired. Mrs Tucker was not at all happy. Her conversation was more rambling, but full of meaning nonetheless. She said she felt 'gone, out of this world'. 'You cannot live forever, so here's goodbye.' 'This is not life at all.' I asked her why she felt this way. She said there was no 'companionship, no trust at all'. Everybody shouted at each other. She said that they were 'treated so bad'. Certainly the staff seemed harsh. One lady was not attended to, though she called incessantly to be taken to the toilet. Indeed for the period of an hour that I sat in the room only domestic staff doing the cleaning of the floors and the corridors said anything to the people inside the room.

Mrs Tucker said the staff did not trouble at all about them. They were too busy doing other things. They polished the floor so much you could 'easily fall down and break your neck'. You couldn't lie down when you wanted to because they were cleaning, yet they shone a torch in your face in the early hours of the morning, and pushed you to do things. She was 'fed up to the knocker' having to beg. She wanted to 'get away, go out of this place'. 'I must get away,' she repeated.

Six months later, when I called again, she was sitting in the same place. She was more placid than before, and pleased to see me. Her attention had become absorbed in the situation of her neighbours and she indicated a great deal of interest in them. She told me about each in turn when they did something striking. Her comment was usually sympathetic. The room had a heavy smell of incontinence. One women kept getting out of her chair and then sitting down again. One spoke frequently out loud in German. Another called incessantly to go to the toilet and another actually made a mess on the floor. 'God help them all!' exclaimed Mrs Tucker. A man 'in a robe' she said, had come and held a service. 'God help them all,' he had said.

On this last occasion I tried to ask the same questions as I had done ten years previously about reminiscence, life satisfaction and so on. It was difficult to keep Mrs Tucker's attention to the questions, but her reponses were clear enough. She spoke with much affection about her family, one son in particular, and said somebody came weekly. But her life now she said was not a happy one. This was 'not her home'. She stressed how 'bored' she was. When I asked whether she expected pleasant things to happen, she said she would not be there much longer. She felt so tired, her back so painful. When I asked her whether she was satisfied with her past life, she hesitated then said no, because of what had happened to her at the end. But she later said her life had been good. She said she thought a great deal about the past. She mentioned her 'good husband' and her 'little house'. But she could not say that reminiscence made her feel good. Again, it was the losses she had suffered that dominated her conversations about the past. When I asked whether she would change anything in her past life, she began speaking about how her father fell down the pit. She mentioned many other losses spontaneously—the death of her husband, the death of her mother, the loss of her old house, people stealing her things in the sheltered housing. Despite her 'confusion' her conversation was very similar to ten years previously.

When I spoke to the officer in charge on this same occasion she said that Mrs Tucker was as 'happy as could be expected'. She was 'very confused' and could be 'naughty'. Justifying her policy of putting the 'confused' together, she said they were more likely to help one another. The other residents were much less tolerant, and you could not blame them. She also said that Mrs Tucker's family visited regularly.

Two months later Mrs Tucker was admitted to the geriatric ward in the local hospital and from there was transferred to a psychogeriatric ward in a more distant hospital. She died a few weeks later. 'Oh yes, poor Annie,' said a member of staff in the old people's home when I next called, 'she got very bad indeed, she must have done to have gone there.' Again she stressed how very good and supportive Mrs Tucker's family had been.

Despite Mrs Tucker's increasing mental deterioration there was a great deal of continuity between her attitudes in 1971 and 1981. She had come from a poor but close family and had had a hard life. Her memories were dominated by experience of loss. In 1971 she was very unhappy about her situation. She did not like living alone and wished again she could be with her family. She felt depressed and unwell. Over the following ten years she continued to complain about feeling unwell and lonely, and when in 1980 she was finally taken into care because of her inability to look after herself, her situation soon deteriorated further. She was placed among the 'psychogeriatric' residents. She experienced the treatment that they were given as a further loss, a loss of 'real life'. 'This is not life at all,' she said. She was rational enough to understand what was being done to her—and to the others living there. Her great quality, concern for others, remained undiminished.

Subsequent History of Other Cases

Few longitudinal details are available on the other four people identified in this study who shared the same attitude of being unable to bear reminiscing, but they all consistently bear out a negative prognosis on subsequent life adjustment. Mr Cox as already mentioned died quickly, as he wished to. Mr Bungay by contrast lived another eight years. I only saw him on brief occasions over this time and am unable to comment to any degree on his last years. Certainly he maintained his negative and complaining attitudes, and continued to be ridiculed both by the warden and other tenants, who thought his negative view of life to be over-exaggerated. He was described by one tenant as 'a malingerer'. Mr Bungay did not appear to let this bother him and held on to his negative views on life.

Perhaps his personality had always been gloomy and little adaptable to change. At least he had insight into his problem. He described himself as a 'poor mixer'. Also his complaints about the siting of the particular sheltered housing scheme he lived in, far from all amenities, were quite justified, and he was prepared to take some action, writing letters to the bus service, whereas other people seemingly were not. On the other hand he gained little of the benefits that were available from living in a sheltered housing scheme. For example, he did not participate in the group outings that the warden organized.

Mrs Jackson also regretted moving away from her old neighbourhood. In her case the housing department took note and in 1972 moved her to a new scheme which was built nearer to where she used to live. She was also admitted to the geriatric department and attended the day hospital for rehabilitation, but sadly without any obvious benefit. She remained very depressed. In 1974 she was moved to an old people's home and died the year afterwards. I do not know whether she received any anti-depressant medication. She might have been helped by it. When I last saw her she was very unhappy indeed, and seemed totally unsure of herself.

Mrs Kitchen was the odd person out in the group as she was not depressed in 1971. I did not see her again but later heard that she became mentally disturbed. On the warden's account and that of her neighbours she became increasingly worried and nervous and had hallucinations. She was admitted into a psychiatric hospital in 1973, remained there and died nearly a year later. She was 78. Further details I could not obtain and detailed speculation would be unjustified. Possibly though her symptoms were of a psychotic depressive illness. In retrospect, therefore, it seemed much more significant that she said she tried to avoid reminiscence because the comparison with the present made her sad. Such an attitude seems to be indicative of maladjustment and the evidence from this study is quite convincing that it should be taken as a warning sign by those in the helping professions.

Chapter 9

Towards Integrity

Gerontology is a mutli-disciplinary subject combing both pure and applied study of ageing and old age. Its recent rapid growth however, has been fuelled by awareness of the growing numbers of the very old within the population and an accompanying fear of increased frailty and disability. A practical and problem-oriented bias is especially true of work within the UK. The predominant language has been of 'crisis', 'rising tides' and 'impending disaster'. Considerable imagination has been applied to old age, but focussed largely on solving problems of health and social services provision to larger numbers of disabled people. Partly as a result of this emphasis, old age is sometimes spoken of as if it were an undesirable time of life, and a society with large numbers of older people within it thereby unfortunate and somehow unnatural.

Yet old age is natural and it would be more in accord with contemporary values to judge it good fortune to live to be old and to enjoy for many years a time of leisure for which one has worked hard all one's life. Problems of chronic physical and mental disability do occur but at a far later stage in life than most people appreciate, and to by no means everyone. The problem, or rather challenge, is the one Busse highlighted in his statement on depression, quoted in Chapter 2, that of making life 'meaningful' in later life. What does one do when the more obvious goals of career, accumulating property and raising a family have subsided? As many literary writers have realized, consideration of old age forces us to ask fundamental questions about life, no longer so easy to avoid. It is a time for having answers to life's questions.

There are no satisfactory models of 'successful ageing'. There are different approaches and definitions used in research—independence in the activities of daily living, observed stability and lifestyle in the face of external change, expressed contentment with life, absence of symptoms of mental illness—and it is clearly false to assume that they are merely different approaches to an underlying unitary concept of 'adjustment'. A choice has to be made by each investigator. Erikson's concept of 'integrity', however, remains one of the few attempts to provide an ideal model of old age, based on the principles of an acceptance of one's own history, a universal rather than egocentric perspective on human life, and a loss of fear of death. It remains valuable as a standard, however hard it may be to achieve in reality. For it does confront key issues about growing old that are often ignored by gerontologists.

Death, for example, must be central to the interests of the study of old age. Much gerontological writing on the contrary almost gives the impression that death is an avoidable rather than inevitable conclusion to old age. But the old know well enough that their life is nearing an end. As those researchers who have investigated attitudes to death readily acknowledge, older people do not generally share the same hesitancy and reluctance to discuss death. They talk about openly and in personal terms (e.g. Lieberman and Tobin, 1983). Coming to terms with one's 'finitude' is a key feature of adjustment to old age (see Munnichs, 1966). This is manifested in a number of ways, one being the process of 'tidying up'. Concern with what will happen to property, and attempts to distribute some of it to children, friends and others represent a recognition of mortality and a wish to leave the world with some orderly distribution of the products of a life well-lived.

People also are generally concerned with what will happen to their society after they die. Yet if society is to be so different from the one one has known, if indeed it appears likely to overthrow or indeed already have otherthrown the values that were so important in guiding one's own life, it can be harder to die. This is the issue, raised already in Chapter 3, of the greater difficulty of adjustment to ageing in a fast changing society. It needs courage and imagination to see through the different manifestations of human interests and activities and to perceive an underlying constancy. Erikson refers to 'a comradeship with the ordering ways of distant times and different pursuits ... Although aware of the relativity of all the various lifestyles which have given meaning to human striving, the possessor of integrity is ready to defend the dignity of his own style against all physical and economic threats' (Erikson, 1965, p.260). It is not to deny that there are differences. It is to be confident enough about one's own life to defend the course it has taken, yet be able at the same time to tolerate other ways as well. Self-acceptance and acceptance of others go hand in hand.

Judgements on the value of one's own past life do become inevitable in old age as new opportunities diminish. It is often too late to start again or to make amends for wrongs done. A sense of fulfilment is crucial to happiness in late life. 'What makes old age hard to bear,' said Somerset Maugham, 'is not a failing of one's faculties, mental and physical, but the burden of one's memory' (Maugham, 1959).

Because of its current problem-oriented focus recent gerontological studies have been reticent about analysing and discussing ideal models of old age. In this chapter I have therefore deliberately chosen to present three case studies of individuals who seemed to me to have arrived close to Erikson's standard of integrity. The choice I stress is a personal one. All three are people who lived a long time and who therefore I learned to know well. They were also all people from whom I learned a good deal personally and whose courage I wondered at. That they had coped so well with the difficulties they had been presented with in life gave them for me a special aura.

In the presentation of their cases I have followed the same format as in the previous chapters. The focus as with the others is on their use of reminiscence. In this the three cases show considerable variation. Mrs Parsons, the first case, clearly belongs among those who treasure their memories, despite the difficulties of her past life, nursing a sick son and husband. She has regrets about the way she has lived, but feels also that she has learned a lot from her life. She experiences a sense of wisdom and she indicates that she has achieved this only recently through a period of life-reviewing. Although almost always alone, she is not lonely. Unafraid of death, she has a Socratic attitude of curiosity and confidence about what might lie beyond. She does not glorify the past to the expense of the present. She looks beyond the superficialities of human life to fundamental issues. She hopes for improvement both for herself and for humankind.

Mr Norton by contrast says he is not concerned with the past any more. Scarred by the experiences of the First World War, he has been led to question and demolish in his own mind many of the authority figures of his young days, the aristocracy, the politicians and the clergy. Yet he has not despaired. He still believes that the higher faculties of human beings—in particular their rationality—can lead them to a better world. He identifies closely with this hope. He looks at life 'scientifically' and seeks practical solutions to problems. He includes in this consideration his own situation, increasingly infirm and isolated.

Mrs Manners was one of the most disabled people in the sample, crippled by rheumatoid arthritis. Yet in many ways she appears the most youthful and vigorous of the people I interviewed. Uncomplaining, despite severe pain and discomfort, she has won the admiration of those around her. Unassuming, quiet and gentle she is an inspiration to others. Her views on the past, present and the future are harmonious. She counts her blessings. She has developed remarkably firm religious beliefs of a spiritualist nature in mid-life, which she says have banished her earlier excessive fears of death. Her attitudes to the world around, and to the young in particular, are tolerant. Although treasuring the memories of her happy life, she warns against an over-emphasis on reminiscence and the dangers of 'living in the past'.

Taken together these cases of 'successful ageing' both demonstrate the importance of integrating past experiences, and at the same time the value of living in the present and with an eye to the future. It is the continuity of past, present and future that appears important. No element should be stressed to the detriment of the others. Sometimes the needs of the past, for resolution of painful memories, predominate, sometimes the present, for particular everyday concerns, or even the future to clarify sources of inspiration. But none should be excluded permanently or prematurely. Even if it causes pain one has to face all perspectives.

It would be unwise of me to go too far beyond the remit of this book's focus on reminiscence, and make further suggestions about the sources of successful adaptation in later life. Nevertheless it is worth observing that all these three cases demonstrate the importance of a faith or belief. Such a faith need not be expressed in conventionally religious terms. Indeed both Mrs Parsons and Mrs Manners express unconventional beliefs. Nor need it appear religious at all. Mr

Norton expresses his faith in a 'natural philosophy'. Yet they all have belief systems which they have made their own and which are central to their thinking and give their life a sense of coherence. Moreover, they also have hope in a better future for mankind. Theorists on adaptation to old age have stressed the importance of preserving self-esteem (e.g. Lieberman and Tobin, 1983; Coleman, 1984). But it may be that what is important in later life is not only or even principally self-esteem in the conventional sense, that is what one thinks about oneself in comparison to others (i.e. whether one is competent, intelligent, beautiful etc.), but being able to make sense of life in general and seeing meaning and purpose within it. Others of course have pointed to the importance of a sense of meaning and a philosophy of life in human adaptation (e.g. Frankl, 1963; Antonovsky, 1979; Sherman, 1984). Yet they remain relatively neglected topics in comparison to their importance.

Mrs Parsons

Mrs Parsons was a person with whom I developed especially close bonds of affection. She was in fact the very first individual I approached with the idea for my study and on whom I tried out various pilot questionnaires. After I left London we corresponded regularly until her death eight years from the time I was first introduced to her.

She lived in a ground floor flat in a new housing complex in the centre of London where she had moved a few years before. There was a striking contrast between the busy street life outside and the quietness of her room. The sitting room was spartan in the extreme, containing very few objects, just two simple armchairs, a small table, and not a picture around the walls. A few years later I asked myself, in the notes I jotted down after every conversation, whether I had really noticed before just how bare her room had always been. The room was also rather dark as little light came in from the street. Mrs Parsons had not tried to brighten it up. She had little money, but the emptiness did not seem the result of poverty, but a deliberate choice which reflected her personality. Just as she disliked noise, and being with many people together— she would never go to the television room—so what she saw around her had to be uncluttered also. Of much greater importance was what went on inside her. The 16PF personality questionnaire that she filled in for me highlighted her exceptional qualities: reserved, serious, imaginative, free-thinking, self-sufficient, but also tense.

In the beginning I was drawn to Mrs Parsons in part because she seemed to fit perfectly the needs of my study as I then understood it. She would speak readily about her past life, but also in a self-consciously reflective way, pondering the nature of her thoughts. In one of our first conversations she described her memories of the past as being 'like a pattern, all rolled out behind'. She said she could 'pick them out one by one'. This integrated nature of her memories intrigued her and she asked me, 'do others have the same thoughts?'. She said she liked old age, and commented that her mental powers appeared to get clearer in later life rather than deteriorate. Her habit of involving me in her thoughts—she wanted to know what I thought of things that she had done or had happened to her, she asked my views on religious issues, on evolution, on life after death and so on—made a close tie between us, and I grew very fond of her. She was a little cross-eyed, with a wry smile and an almost mischievous manner. What she taught me from her own experience has remained with me as lessons to remember—although as hard to put into practice as she found too.

When I first met her she was 76 years old and had lost her husband 14 years before. Her life had had a lot of sadness in it. She described her childhood as being 'very unhappy'. They had been poor, but much worse were her memories of her father as a 'cruel' and 'drunken' man who used to beat her mother, who she described as an 'angel, a very, very good person'. Mrs Parsons was the only daughter but she had four brothers. The happiest years of her life had been when her husband to be was courting her, but her only son was born with deformed kidneys, and she had to nurse him for 15 years before he died. Her husband too was an ill man in the last years of his life with cancer and needed Mrs Parsons' constant attention. After his death she had gone 'through a dreadful time'.

'... my husband and I were so close together that when he died it was as if a bit of me—I'd died too—and it was like a bit of me wasn't there any more, and I still think that bit of me is gone ...'

On one of the questionnaires I gave her to fill in she summed up the hardest things she had to face in life as 'my son's painful short life, my husband's painful illness, and being left alone afterwards, with no-one to talk to, no-one to care for, and no-one to care for me'.

She said to me that it was only recently that she had come to terms with the losses in her life.

'... it's only been in the last 12 months I should think that I've felt so peaceful, you know ... I don't mind now if I don't go out, only to get my shopping, I don't mind a bit, whereas before I was utterly miserable at the idea of having to stay in this room and do nothing but read a book ...'

At many points in her conversation she referred to a resolution of previous problems in her life, a sense of fulfilment, of completion.

'... it's awfully strange, isn't it, to think we're born and we go all through that, all the ups and downs, the worries and the troubles, and we end up like this. As if we've done our work, we're complete. I can't describe it very well, but there's nothing else to do anymore. [That must be a nice feeling?] Yes it is, it's all done, and you can just sit back, and well, you don't have to worry any more. You've lost all the people that were near and dear to you, there's no-one else that matters all that much, and as I say, you can just stop thinking all about it ...'

The sense she conveyed was of an inner peace, reached after much turmoil. An intense period of life review seemed very close at hand. In the first conversation that I recorded with her I asked her whether she often thought about the past.

'... oh yes, that's all I do do ... yes I think back further and further and think about all the things that happened ...'

Signs of turmoil were still there. Sometimes she had to resist thinking back.

'... if I get a mood coming on that I'm looking back and thinking of all the sorrowful things, I kind of shut my mind up against it, because it's more than I can stand to think of the sufferings of my own child and my husband, and it's no good thinking of it, is it? ... I try to black it out in my mind, and I start thinking of something else, which is best, isn't it?...'

Acceptance, however, was a major theme in the attitudes she expressed to her past. For example, a striking memory, terrifying in its vividness, was of how she had seen her favourite wax doll destroyed as a child. Yet it was noticeable that there was no anger or resentment expressed.

'... the other day I was sitting here, and I was thinking back when I was quite a wee girl, I remember that I was run over by a man on a bicycle, and all the children went running down to my mother, and they were calling out "your Alice has been run over," and of course my mother flew to the door and the man was holding me in his arms. Then they got me upstairs, it was only a little cut somewhere because the bike went over me, and when they got me upstairs the man went out and he bought me a most beautiful doll, a huge wax doll. Do you know, I can see that doll now, with lovely pink cheeks and fair curly hair. It was a lovely doll, and I adored it and loved it, because we were very poor then, I was a child—I never had a doll, never had enough food really, never mind a doll. And anyway, one day to my horror I went into the kitchen and a boy was in there holding my doll in front of the fire and all the wax was dripping, and I began to scream, and he sat there and he wouldn't let me take it until the wax was all melted ... and I was thinking about that. It doesn't matter now, I don't mind a scrap, but at that time I was really broken hearted to think that my dear little doll just dripped and dripped away, because it was pure wax you see, and it melted ... he was just some boy that came around, one of my brother's friends, only a little boy, I don't suppose he knew any different. It was quite fun to him, seeing the wax dripping away, but I was thinking about it the other day, I was thinking what a terrible thing it was, but I don't mind any more, but it was pretty awful for a child of about six, that's all I was, six or seven ... I can still see the doll and the wax dripping, and the way the boy held it from me and wouldn't let me take it. Of course it would have been no good if I had got it away from him, because it was half melted when I discovered it. But you see, children are like that, aren't they. Just thoughtlessness, and I don't suppose he dreamt that I'd be so upset, because I was about it.'

She even expressed reconciliation with her father despite the unhappy memories of childhood she had. She did not hate him. (She'd been the only one in the family who had gone to see him on his death bed.) She tried to understand him, there had been something wrong with him.

On a number of occasions she expressed a sense of genuine acceptance of her past life with all its difficulties. Speaking of her married life and the sorrows she had known, she said

'... I wouldn't miss it, not for the world, although I had a lot of worry with my boy being so ill, you see, and I was nearly distracted at times, but with all that I'm glad I had it. Because if I hadn't had that, I should have had nothing, should I ...'

She expressed the same thought on another occasion.

'... I'd do it all over again. I know he (my husband) was frightfully ill and my son was very, very ill and they suffered a lot, but I wouldn't forego the happiness. I don't know whether I can explain it, but I've had the happiness which made up for the other, and I'm glad that I had that happiness, because it was something, wasn't it? And I can look back on that part, I get a pleasure that I've had that happiness.'

This deep sense of acceptance—perhaps the fruit of a successful life review process—allowed her to see old age in a positive light.

'... it seems as if it all had to be, right from the beginning, because one thing led into another. That led into something else, and so it went on, a pattern, and, now in fact I'm quite peaceful about it all, except when I start to think, then it wakes it all up again. But on the whole I'm very much at peace, and I like my old age, because I can sit back now and think, well, all my worries are over and nothing more need I worry about. I've no need to worry about sickness or money or making ends meet and all that kind of thing, that's all gone, it's rather nice, you know.'

She knew that there were things to be afraid of in old age—in fact she expressed them in her answer to one of the questions I asked her to fill in. She wrote, 'The main problems I would say for most old people are loneliness, people not caring about them, becoming fragile, being treated as children in some cases, or being classed as stupid, and being told what to do'. But she was much less afraid than before. She had developed in later life a strong sense of trust.

Her happiest memories centred on her husband.

'... I like to think of things my husband used to say and the way he used to talk to me, those are the things I like to think of.'

'... the other evening I was sitting here and my mind went back to when I first knew my husband and how he used to meet me. We were so happy, and we used to go off to a theatre or something, and it was such a happy time. I think back on that, and sometimes I got to the place first where we had to meet and he would come up behind me and say, "You looking for someone?" and I think all that, silly things you know.'

'... I had such a good husband. He was such a kind man, and so considerate in every way, I couldn't have had a better husband, so that is something to be thankful for ...'

Some years later she told me how 'shy' she'd been when they had first got married, and that she would not let her husband see her naked. She had thought on this afterwards, and attributed it to the trauma she had experienced as a child bathing in front of her brothers. She smiled as she remembered the things her husband said. He said he 'wouldn't swop her for all the money in the world, but he wouldn't have another like her!'.

Despite her sense of acceptance, Mrs Parsons had a number of regrets about her past life, and this in fact was one of the most interesting characteristics about her reminiscence. Her regrets were creative in that she felt she had learned from her past life, and this gave her now a sense of improvement. She had also learned lessons that she could pass on to others.

'... yes, I think that if we all did a bit more thinking in our younger days and pulled ourselves to bits and analysed ourselves, and became wise to our faults, and tried to lead better lives and be kinder to people. I seem to have learned all that. Because when you are young, you know, you're very very thoughtless, I know I was. I was very thoughtless, and I didn't think about things as I should have done. I used to just not bother about things much, just went sailing on in my own way, and didn't worry much about anything, and then when I got married my troubles started. Woke me up with a jerk then, and I had to stop and think ...'

'... I wish I'd been a better person, I wish I'd been more tolerant, because I suppose it was the worry on my mind, I used to get very upset and agitated and nervy. I suppose it was all the worry of my boy. I look back now and I think well, if it had to happen again now, I wouldn't get in that nervous state, I'd be more in control, but then we don't have another chance, do we? Well I don't think we learn much until we get old and then it's too late. You see, if I could live my life over again, I would be a different person. I would take everything as it came and I would get on with it. And I wouldn't allow myself to get nervous and frightened and upset because now I know it's no use getting in those states because it doesn't make things any better, does it? You don't help anyone by getting frightened and upset and wondering what's going to happen.'

'... I've learned to guard my thoughts more. You see, at one time I used to think a thing and say it, I was so outspoken, and I only had to think of something and I used to spurt it out. Some things I shouldn't have done, I suppose, but now I don't do that any more, because I think sometimes you don't mean to hurt a person but you do hurt them by being outspoken. And yet I like to be honest, I don't like to think one thing and say another. But I think stop and think before you speak, although I hate hypocrisy and dishonesty, but yet you mustn't say what you think. Because it's hurtful. The trouble is, I'm either all or nothing, that's my nature ... you should have a middle course, don't you think?'

'... I didn't start to think until I was quite old. I used to take life just as it came, and not think anything about it, but when I got older I suppose I got some sense and I could think then clearly and I think then you see where you've gone wrong in your life ... I don't know what I could have done, but I wish I'd been a better person, you know. I wish I'd been kinder to people and stopped and listened more, but I was so intent on going through life, you know straight on and not looking sideways. But now I see I could have been a better person and I could have done more good. I could have gone out of my way to have done good to people, but now I'm too tired to do any good, you know.'

Critics of the importance of the life review concept, as McMahon and Rhudick, argue that such questioning of one's behaviour in the past is typical of 'obsessive, compulsive people who, we may suspect, have been reviewing their past behaviour in the same judgemental and evaluative way all their lives' (McMahon and Rhudick, 1967, p.73). Certainly Mrs Parsons displayed some characteristics which might make one think of her as obsessive. For instance, the questioning she subjected herself to in regard to the care she gave her child and husband seemed excessive:

'... I did all I could for them. I don't think I could have done any more to help them during their illnesses, and when they were well, but I still feel that I could have done more. But I don't know what. But I feel I should have done more, I wanted to do more, that kind of feeling, and I feel that if ever I had my chance over again I would be so different. In what way I'd be different I don't know, but I suppose well, they wouldn't have liked me to have been lonely and sorrowful over them, would they, so it's awfully difficult to know what to do isn't it?

Also she described herself as a worrier:

'...well I'm always worried more or less, you see being alone so much we think about things and we kind of magnify them and they grow so big that it's really nothing to worry about, but I suppose we think about it and think about it because we've got nothing else to think about. And it gets bigger and bigger and bigger until you think your head's going to pop out or something, but I'm not so bad as I used to be. I used to worry terribly. I used to worry in case I hadn't enough things and all that, but now I don't bother any more, because I think, well I've got so old now that everything will last out, you know.'

But on the other hand, Mrs Parsons regarded herself as having become a 'worrier' in response to the stresses of her married life.

'... I was child that didn't ever use to cry. I used to take it all in my stride ...'

Certainly on the 16PF Cattell personality inventory she appeared more as 'expedient' than 'conscientious' and only slightly 'apprehensive and prone to guilt'. The characteristics on which she scored most highly were those relating to introversion. She was, or had become, a nervous person, a 'worrier', and these indeed were the characteristics she blamed herself for principally in the past—not being sufficiently calm in the face of troubles, speaking out rather than holding her tongue when she was upset.

Her wish to become a better person was deeply and calmly expressed and closely tied with her religious thoughts. These gave her hope for improvement. She made the association directly in the way she spoke about it.

'... but as I say when you get old then you stop and think, when you're young you just race on pell mell, don't you, through life. You just race through it and you don't think this way and you don't think that way, you just race straight on, and when you get about 60 you stop and think. You can see then where you've gone wrong and what you should have done and what you shouldn't have done, but then it's too late, unless we have another life and are born again.'

Another person who visited her regularly in the same years that I did was a young woman who was a follower of the Maharishi Yogi and his methods of meditation. She also spoke with Mrs Parsons about Hindu beliefs in reincarnation which she found interesting. Mrs Parsons explained it to me as follows:

'... you see, the point is that in the previous life your character is formed, that's the way I look at it ... in the next one you've got a better character. For instance, if I live my life over again I would strive to be a better person and I would know what to do. I wouldn't go rushing forward, I would stop and think, which is the right way and which is the best way, that's what I would do if I lived again. But you see probably it is all experience, perhaps the experience I've had in this life, if I were born again, I might be born with a better understanding, you see what I mean, having experienced my failures in this life. I do certainly believe that we go on, I don't believe we just die and that's an end of us, I do believe that there's something after this, but what form it takes of course we don't know.'

She therefore saw reincarnation as a hopeful doctrine.

'... well I suppose some people are born wicked, well they're not born wicked but as they grow up they're vicious, these louts that walk about today, well that must be their character, mustn't it, to be like that. They must feel like that to act like it. They can't help it. Well as they get reborn and reborn that might cure itself and get better and better, and each time they are born again they are a little bit better till in the end, whatever the end is, I don't know, they are a much better person ...'

Religion was a subject of absorbing interest to her, and illustrated her free thinking and disrespect for traditional thought. She had rejected the images of God she had been taught as a child.

'... I can't think of God as God, as he's pictured to us. I know mind you that there's some powerful force at work, but I can't think of God as the church teaches him, do you see what I mean?...'

'... there's a lot that you can't take in, I can't. Your own common sense won't let you take it in, such as Adam and Eve in the garden. Well, it's a load of rubbish to my way of thinking, honestly ... I think the majority of it is stories and fables and things that have been made up as time goes on ...'

'... but I do believe that there's someone or something very powerful that does guide us. But to be able to pick out any one of these millions of people and say, you know, to know all about us and all our troubles and all our worries, it's impossible, isn't it really, don't you think so. Of all the millions in the world, millions and millions of people, and yet he knows, according to the church, God knows each one of us, but I can't think that. But I think when we pray, if we do pray earnestly enough, we can call something into our environment. Yes, that helps us. I do think that whether by praying we pick something up or we contact something, I don't know, but I do think that we do contact something when we pray very earnestly. It seems as if we have got to get into such a state of mind that we can reach whatever it is that God, or whatever it is that is this power.'

'... I believe and I think that when our loved ones do die I think that there is another life and I think that they are still around to influence us and guide us and that's how I think.'

She described how she had vivid dreams of her husband, as if he were talking to her, which meant a lot to her. She described too how her husband had had similar dreams of their son after he had died.

She was also sceptical of the Maharishi. She had made this clear to her other visitor.

'... she said he was trying to help the world, to think differently and think in the right channels. I said to her why doesn't he start in his own country, India is in such a bad state ... and she said, "Oh well, he wants the world to get the message first and then help would come to India". And if that was me and I was the Maharishi, I should help my own country first, wouldn't you? After all, charity begins at home, doesn't it? Probably that's the reason, because she said they're in a frightful state, they're starving and stealing and looting and everything going on, so probably that's what it is, but this way he's getting the money in, he's also had the Beatles in, hasn't he?'

But this criticism did not stop her from picking out aspects of Eastern religious thought that attracted her.

'... Karma is everything you've done in all your lives, you die, you come back, you die and you come back, you die and come back—and you have to suffer for all that you've done in those past lives, each life you lead that you come back to, you have to pay for what you've done in your past lives, and you go on and go on and as you come back of course so you learn and you get a better person through experience, and in the end you don't come back, because you're perfect.'

There was a richness to the way Mrs Parsons described her inner life that made her retreat from the world appear attractive. When she did speak about contemporary society it was with a certain detachment. She expressed herself cautiously, pointing out that to really speak on matters such as Ireland, one had to see for oneself. The views one received from outside were often prejudiced. She did draw some comparisons between past and present society and saw both positive and negative points. The poor had suffered badly in the inter-war years. But that general suffering was behind her, just as her own personal suffering.

'... I think people were happier, they weren't so self-centred, as they are now, and they weren't flying about trying to find pleasures, they were simpler I suppose. I'm talking about the working class, not about the rich, because they had their pleasures all the time, didn't they? But the working class I think, they didn't get much and they didn't expect much, and if they got their daily bread, well they thought they were lucky. Of course you don't know the hungry 1930s, do you? It's a good thing you don't. They used to parade the streets with banners, give us work, you know, just starving with no dole, nothing, no relief of any kind, and men used to form a column and walk through the streets—"the hungry '30s", I expect you've heard of it. People were hungry, they really were. Margarine was only threepence a pound in those days, and you know they couldn't afford to buy it, it just shows you, doesn't it. And yet the rich went on in the same old way, enjoying everything, wasting enough that would have kept a family for a week. Used to go to the dustbins. I know, I've heard it. It all seems very wrong, doesn't it. But as I say, that doesn't bother me any more. That's all gone, yes, it's all gone, as though it's never been. Like a dream, good thing too, isn't it. Because you could harp on those things and get really unhappy, couldn't you.'

She defended her way of life. A voluntary visitor who had taken her out once a month had jokingly called her 'a recluse' because she did not want to got out any more or even mix with the other residents in the television room. She had thought about it afterwards and felt the negative connotations of the word and decided to write him a letter. She told me what she had written.

'I've been giving thought to what you said, that you think I'm a recluse. Indeed you are very wrong. Because I don't like talking scandal and gossip, that does not say that I am a recluse. I have my own powers of thinking which I use for my own benefit. I like to look, which I do, and I like to go quietly on with my own life ... I admit I don't make friends easily, and it takes me quite a while to get to know anyone so that I can talk to them freely, but that doesn't make me a recluse. Some people can come along and they start to chatter away, but I'm not like that. We're all made different, aren't we?'

For the following six years until her death Mrs Parsons was dogged with numerous health problems. Thrombosis in her leg led to an initial spell in hospital and continued problems with her blood circulation, which also affected her hands badly, together with episodes of asthma, led to further stays in hospital. Then problems were diagnosed with her thyroid but she refused to go into hospital again. In hospital, she said, she had too many others around her all the time and that 'disturbed her thinking'. Dermatitis in her hands caused her a lot difficulties as well. She was also found to have progressive cancer of the breast.

Three years later she did go into hospital again for two periods of a month each for rest and therapy. She again had refused to go in at first, and once when she felt she was being treated badly she threatened to leave. But the hospital staff had given her a good time on her birthday, and she felt embarrassed at having been so truculent. She finally died quite suddenly following a stroke. The warden gave me the news. It was better so, she said, as Mrs Parsons would not have liked going in a home.

In these years I visited Mrs Parsons on six occasions and we exchanged a number of letters—she wrote to me eight times in all. In comparison to our first conversations she spoke relatively little about the past, but expressed appreciation of having been able to talk to someone about her life. After I had finished my initial study and was working in Holland she mentioned this in letters to me on two separate occasions.

'... I often think of you, and our talks. I wonder sometimes that you had the patience to listen to me, and hear all my secrets.'

'... I am thinking of you very much and the happy talks we have had, and of how freely I have been able to tell you things I could not have told anyone else.'

She took a great interest in my writing and hoped that the book that I would write about reminiscence would be a success.

She continued to draw lessons from life based on her own personal experiences. She consoled me with my own difficulties. She stressed how one should be thankful for the good things in life. Health, for instance, was a 'blessing'. The last time we spoke—I had then been married a year—she told me seriously,

'... love and friendship are the most important things in life. Don't be too busy. You will regret it later. Cherish each other. That's heaven.'

Despite her increasing physical frailty she stressed a number of times how much she liked old age. Her worries were over and she could see things clearly. She continued to speak a lot about religious themes and the nature of life after death. Natural evolution also absorbed her as a subject.

'... supposing you were just a tiny bit in a pond, a little speck, it would take millions and millions of years to get us to what we are now, with eyes and hearing and all our other faculties. And is it possible that a human being could develop. I wonder if we should develop any more?'

She struggled with her physical ailments but in the end accepted them. She wrote to me about her problems.

'... I hate the idea of going into hospital again, but I suppose that the doctor at the hospital knows what is best!! ... they were very kind in the hospital, but I would rather be at home, but I shall just have to be patient, and take things as they come along. This is not so hard to do, when one is my age. I think old people just submit to things, don't you?'

Her skin problems upset her particularly, and in the end she turned for other help. She wrote to me on a later occasion.

'... my hands got in such a bad state and the hospital did not seem able to do much except to keep the condition down with the help of ointments and so on. I was rather depressed about it all, as the hospital doctors thought there was no cure, and told me not to put them in water, so you can imagine my misery, at not being able to do things. I wrote to a psychic healer, whom I knew some years ago, and asked for help. She is a very psychic person and is sending vibrations out to help me. This has been going on for about six weeks, and during the last three weeks my hands are very much better, so much so that on my visit to Middlesex Hospital the doctors told me I need not attend again, as there was a great improvement. I think it caused a surprise. I did not tell them about the psychic part, as I didn't know how they would take it! They said if the trouble started up badly again, I was to go back to them. They were most kind and good, and I feel very grateful for all they did for me ...
'...PS My hands may have healed anyway. That I do not know, but after two years of hospital treatment it makes me wonder.'

Mrs Parsons had reached a remarkable level of integrity. She had come to accept her past life with all its difficulties and achieved tranquillity after much turmoil. She was aware she still had many faults. Her other visitor, the follower of the Maharishi, had told her she was too 'proud' and 'stubborn' and she accepted that. She welcomed the development she had already experienced and wished for more. She wrote in answer to one of the questions on a questionnaire I gave her, 'If you could stay the same age all your life what age would you choose and why?':

'I would not like to stay the same age all my life as to grow older is to expand, and to gain knowledge and understanding, and learn from experience.'

She liked old age. As she put it to me strikingly on one occasion,

'Of course you're very young, you've had no experience yet, but when you get to my age, you'll probably look back, as I do, and you'll see it all like spread out. Marvellous, isn't it really?'

Mr Norton

Mr Norton was 82 years when I first met him living in a first floor flat in north London. He had become increasingly frail and limited in his activities in the previous year, with painful rheumatism in his neck and shoulders and chronic eye inflammation. He received regular home help. Still he did not complain about his health, and would never spontaneously refer to it. His wife had died 15 years previously, they had had no children, and the only relatives with whom he corresponded were his nieces, the children of his dead brother, who lived in America. He had lost contact with his sisters. As a family they had not 'stuck together'.

His attitude to old age was remarkably positive in the circumstances. Questions on the life satisfaction index, for instance, he answered forthrightly and with illustrative comment. 'No' old age was 'certainly not the dreariest time' of his life. Life was more interesting because of increased experience. He certainly could say that he was as happy as when he was younger. 'Mentally' he was happier. He looked forward to new interests in life. It was foolish to be bored. As Bernard Shaw said—he often quoted Shaw—the trouble was one did not live long enough to benefit from experience. The physical decline with ageing he accepted. He looked at it in a 'natural way'. He had a tough life to look back on. Yes, he said, he had expected 'better things' as a young man, but he had given up expecting. Life was what one made it.

He had been born into a Quaker family in Northumberland, but he had broken all Quaker principles by joining the Army just before the First World War. It was not a decision he was proud of. He had to excuse himself.

'. . . I came from Quaker stock. I was taught to detest violence and everything else, and yet I joined the Army. You see circumstances were not too good you know, you hadn't the opportunities you have today. In 1912 I went into the mines. I couldn't make enough money at gardening, horticulture. I was trained to grow plants, greenhouse culture outside as well. My parents got their living from the land. Most Quakers did, and they had their own nursery and raised their own plants—you see I still do it here, it's interest you know. My father was a wizard with plants, and naturally I took a lot of interest in it . . . He nearly went mad when I joined the Army. He said, "Don't think I'll buy you out" you know when I jumped in. I joined in February 1913 . . .'

For Mr Norton the war was a devastating experience. Like Mr Thompson, he had been through the big events.

'When the 1914 war started, I volunteered for service abroad. Was accepted for that quick. Saw it right through. Seems so strange sometimes. I pinch myself you know to see if I'm real or not. I was in the first attack with the tanks at Combray. I was in the first gas attack at Ypres. Lamatinge, Bloodstreak Hill 60, Vimey Ridge. Oh I know them all, I was there two years and eleven months in the field before I got anything and I landed up in hospital...'

Like Mr Thompson, he bore the psychological scars, perhaps even more deeply. Reminiscences of the war were still too painful to him.

'... The army experience, you see, it brutalizes a man, destroys him. It doesn't actually destroy, but it goes a long way. It takes a long time to re-orient himself when he comes back you see. In fact, some people don't. Some don't. You see their experiences have been, what shall we say, so vile, or so alarming, choose any word you like, that they never get over it and they end up in the nuthouse, asylum, or jail or something like this you see. That's what war does to people you know.'

'... It was a dirty business. You see each war I think throws people further back. You see we were practically living in the Stone Age again. That's the way I looked at it. We were just living in holes, covered with lice. I never slept in a bed for about three years, subjected to all this heavily concentrated artillery fire ...'

The quality of his reminiscences of actual events had a vivid, nervous, trembling quality, as if it had been yesterday.

'... We had to wait until it was dark, and then we went into this village, a place called Packard, I think it was, and when it was dark we went forward and down these fields, among these manure heaps, waiting for daylight. Then fix bayonets, and you know I wasn't afraid of anything. Curious, you know. Bullets came sweeping by. Shouting. "You won't hear the one that hits you. Fellows getting knocked out on one side. "Come on for Christ's sake!"—This sort of thing you know, you don't care to recall them really. I do my best to forget it. Can't really forget it, I'm not constituted that way ...'

Mr Norton said he now thought little about the past. He used to think more, he admitted, but now he did not see that it was a good thing to do. He ascribed little or no useful function to reminiscing. 'It leads nowhere.' Still there were things he could not forget. On another occasion he described to me how long it took him to recover himself after the war. He would be getting out of bed in the morning looking for his rifle. There were memories of experiences he would like to cut out. Indeed, he still turned off the TV if things came up which he found painful. Generally he managed successfully to conquer disturbing thoughts so they did not worry him at night any more or make life difficult for him. If he did think back on his life, it was the idyllic world of his childhood he preferred to focus on. What stood out was:

'... childhood, country bred you know, and a natural observer. I used to take a delight in all these things. Collecting birds' eggs. Studying nature. Making observations ... there was a friend of my father, an old survivor of the Indian mutiny, he was quite an old man, I was just a boy then, he used to talk to me about all kinds of things. He gave me a glimmering of what it was all about, natural philosophy ...'

Observation and delight in observation were Mr Norton's strong qualities. Even the army had been useful in this regard.

'... My father was a hell of a stickler for what was true, and the search for truth leads you into some strange places. And then when you're in the field you see you meet people from all parts of the world. It's an education in itself. You meet different fellows and they had no television. They gave you their actual experience. They didn't know whether they would be alive or dead the next day. People used to come clean then you see. Whether you were an officer or a private soldier you were all in together. One thing about the British Army, they stand by each other. We all did too ...'

Mr Norton had learned to observe human nature, and this was his most powerful point. Man had to accept the truth about himself. Idealism was dangerous. There was much that was awful and brutal in life, but in improving the world one had to start from the right premises. Scientifically observed premises. Such thoughts led him to his strongest utterances. For instance, he moved from describing the nature of trench warfare to a condemnation of Christian preachers.

'... There was a bloke there, dead, and I was tying him up to this tree because we were standing on him in the trench... The officer said, "Put that bloody man down, he's no bloody use, he's dead". Well I said, "We're treading on him". See the sort of type? You wouldn't introduce a fellow like that to your sister you know! Anyway, as a soldier he's trained that way. See if you have a background, come from a good home, doesn't do you no good. See what I mean, life's real. It's about time people looked up. What gets me are these jaspers going about saying, "Love your neighbour". You shouldn't do anything of the sort ...'

He expressed the same thought on another occasion.

'... The Second World War was different. You fight all day and maybe never see an enemy at all ... it's technical warfare you know, the latest gadgets and all that. It's bloody murder. This love your neighbour business has all gone by the board you see. The law of life is survival of the fittest, you may as well face it, whether you're in business or any other thing, it's a fact. Human life is parasitic. We live on each other. That's the way I look at it. But some people emphasize the struggle, I don't, I would like to ameliorate it if I could...'

He had no time for politicians either.

'... I try to be logical if I can, reasonable. I am not out to reform the world, accept it as it is and try to adapt myself to it. I think that is the most reasonable point of view. Any person who thinks they can reform the world, I think is living under a delusion. You see the problem is so vast, people don't realize. They are misled by these politicians and various other people who know better, but are using them for their own advantage. You will see them in full spate before long, leading up to another election ... instead of playing down to the public they ought to be trying to lift them up. Instead of that, they use them to their own advantage. No-one believes them anymore really. It's gradually breaking through you see to the man in the street that these people are only playing a game. At least that's the way I like to look at it... But the ordinary man has sunk into a sort of apathy. He has been decieved that many times. You try to get them to reason intelligently and apply a bit of logic. They have never heard of it, they have never been taught that way ... It's a case of suppressing the knowledge which ought to reach the man in the street ...'

His cynicism had its origins in the First World War.

'... Lloyd George, he made millions out of armaments with his feed the guns campaign. There was an old woman there in Manchester. She said, "Terrible feeding the guns," she had a big bag of teacakes, she said "I'm going to feed the gunners" ... Feed the guns! Welsh wizard! I know what I'd have done with him if I'd got hold of him. He did very well out of the war. So did Stanley Baldwin, the big steel people. So did the clergy too. "Praise the Lord my dear Augusta, we've won a battle, such a muster. Ten thousand Germans sent below. Praise God from whom all blessings flow!" There is nothing like a bit of soldiering to buck your ideas up, you see life in the raw then ...'

But as the 'observant gardener' he had also seen feet of clay in figures of authority before.

'... The gardener existed on next to nothing, what he could raise for himself on a few plants, and then you've got to ask permission from the people you work for. The gardener was a valuable asset to a country gentleman. He raised all his vegetables for him and worked himself to death just to keep in his small cottage or bothey, or whatever it was. Whereas he'd be a multi-millionaire travelling the world in search of expensive rare plants ... the gardener understands, he knows their little ways. I remember the Kaiser, I remember old King Edward VII, another right lad! I saw what they were doing. I was laying a place out for the chaplain of Lord North. He had a chaplain you see. He could have done with two or three! They'd got it all off you know, those people are no fools. You see they never employ anybody locally, they talk too much ...'

I visited Mr Norton many times, 14 in all in the two years of my study, 1970–71. Sometimes we played chess on his suggestion. His conversation was rarely of a personal kind and I learned little of his life after the First World War. Soldiering, he said, had taken 'the best part' of his life, but he had gone back to gardening eventually, and had worked in this way until he was 71. He spoke of his delight in nature and was proud of the collection of exotic Mexican plants on the balcony of his flat. He alluded often to his wartime experiences, but only occasionally did full blown reminiscence break through.

What he was keen to tell me was his pilosophy of life which he reiterated in various forms. There were common themes. Firstly it was important to accept man's 'animal' origins. He spoke of Darwin with great respect. Life was a struggle for survival. People were basically out for themselves. Men pretended to be different with polite and considerate manners, but the animal principle of 'kill or be killed' was the basic factor. Reformers who did not accept the full weight of this realization were only kidding themselves and others. The advantages of any reform were difficult to weigh up. What led to improvement in one way could cause disaster in others. The problem was too complex. He liked to draw an analogy with the impossibility of writing a computer program to play a perfect game of chess.

He saw 'science' as man's best hope, and by this he meant a respect for truth reached by observation and scientific method. He was suspicious of ideas and theories which were not testable. He expressed a logical positivist and behaviourist philosophy (for example, he dismissed Freud as 'fraudulent'). One should collect facts and stop talking. The main villains in the world he identified as authority figures like politicians, priests and journalists—who kept people in ignorance for their own ends. They exploited and misused the truth, confused people, and manipulated them by means of nationalistic and religious feelings. They made people afraid of knowledge. Many times he linked his views with his experiences in the Great War and how men were influenced by ideas, while their leaders used them for the purpose of profiteering.

He expressed time and again the dilemma which he felt as a personal one. What should a man do who realizes these things? Should he seek how best to fend for himself or should he try to improve things? If a policeman was sensible, he would stand aside when he saw a violent crime being committed. If he was doing his job, he risked his life. He believed that man's intelligence could form a basis for a 'natural religion'. The important thing was to accept the world as it was with all its cruelties and brutalities. There was no meaning or purpose in life to be found. There were no magic or secret revelations. Meaning and purpose had to be created by man's realization of his common humanity. The Christian churches were run by people who did the opposite, 'crooks' who abused their position. He would have no truck with them. His one great hope was that 'intelligence' had not been given a good enough try yet.

Because he knew I was a university student and a psychology student as well, he directed his views to me perhaps the more forcefully. Education was essential to man's improvement. But the centres of learning were still under the influence of the 'monastery' paying more attention to authority rather than the facts around. Television could be a fine means of education, but it was used often only to entertain, playing down to the public rather than trying to elevate them. As a result, people did not know what to believe in. People should be told the facts of life.

'... I would teach them the facts of life, how to adapt themselves to it, but not to bring them up on myths ... the youngsters can't see the wood for the trees—the truth lies in front of them. They should know if they start to play with fire, they'll burn themselves. They ought to be told that. Instead you've got somebody that says, "Oh, she's only young you know", some silly old blackguard sitting on the bench there, who shouldn't sympathize with them at all. You've got to teach them how to live, to adapt themselves, to live in harmony with their neighbours, not love them at all, take them for what they are ...'

At the time, though I listened respectfully to Mr Norton and enjoyed his humourous asides, I did not take him that seriously. The stress on the negative elements of life seemed excessive and I attributed it to his own particular bad experiences in life. I thought he was defensive about his own personal life and his own feelings and I could not understand why he seemed so well adjusted. It was only subsequently that I came to respect his struggle to make sense of the problems of living and of mankind's future.

Also, I was probably initially influenced by knowing that he had registered with a voluntary visiting organization as a person who would appreciate visits from students. Therefore it was rather easy to label him as 'lonely'. But in fact, as he enjoyed discussing philosophy, science and politics (and a game of chess) he had taken the most sensible course of action to bring this about. I also came to appreciate that there was a warmth in his interest for me, and a disinterested concern for my own progress.

I saw him on another four occasions before he died in 1979 aged 91 years. We also corresponded at Christmas times. His views remained essentially the same. Each time we met I found myself struck by the sharpness of his memory and his general mental alertness. The last time I saw him on a visit back from Holland, he said he was virtually housebound. He was eager to hear about my experiences in Holland and surprised to find out that it was so progressive in attitudes and practice. Still critical of politicians, he at least gave Harold Wilson the credit for 'trying'. He repeated how terrible his experiences had been in the First World War and how he would like to forget them. He had gone to war, even though he had been of Quaker stock! Man had an animal nature. A proper scientific study of behaviour was needed but the people were told stories and myths instead.

His room was still very well kept and his plants flourished. For the first time I wrote down in my notes how interesting the pictures around the wall were. They had various literary and scientific associations—I remember a particularly striking etching of Dante meeting Beatrice along the River Arno in Florence. I sensed a connection between his family's Quakerism and his humanistic, natural religion. Rationality had not yet been given a good enough try in the world. This thought allowed him to remain optimistic.

Mrs Manners

Mrs Manners was born in Chelsea in 1898. Her mother died when she was very young and she was adopted by her father's sister who lived in Kensington. She did not speak much about her childhood, but conveyed the impression of a very happy family atmosphere. One of her lifelong pleasures was music, and she had learned to play the piano at an early age. She remembered how, for a few years, the family had lived in Wales and how much she had enjoyed the musical life there. She married after the First World War. Her first child, a boy, died two weeks after birth, but she later had two daughters. Her husband had a successful career in the Post Office and she described their married life as a very harmonious one.

But at the age of 50 Mrs Manners quite suddenly developed rheumatoid arthritis which affected her limbs. Within a month she could not move. The first acute attack faded but she remained largely incapacitated for the rest of her life. She received various treatments and operations. She and her husband moved eventually to a ground floor maisonette. In 1965 her husband died of cancer, and five years later her GP persuaded her to move into a sheltered housing scheme nearby. When I spoke to her at the end of 1969 and the beginning of 1970, she was preparing for an operation to have artificial joints placed in both her knees. A year later she spoke gratefully of 'receiving back' her legs.

I talked with Mrs Manners six times in all from the end of 1969 to the end of 1971. As well as answering my questionnaires, she told me a lot about her views on life in general, but I learned significantly more things about the psychological adjustments she had made in her life when I re-interviewed her ten years later. She was a quiet, gentle and somewhat shy woman who did not wish to press her opinions on others, and her spiritualist beliefs which I only later encouraged her to describe to me came as quite a revelation.

To my questions in the first period that we spoke, her answers were uniformly positive, but expressed carefully and unassertively. She had a favourable view of both her past life and present circumstances. She regarded herself as being especially fortunate, both in her childhood and marriage families. She had a few regrets—she wished she had made more use of opportunities to help other people—but the main things in her life she would not change. All her memories, she said, were very happy ones, she liked to reminisce and she felt she gained support and strength from reminiscence. She thought especially about her married years.

She was clearly a very happy person. Although she would not describe old age as the 'best years of her life', she felt herself to be as happy as when she was younger 'perhaps in a different way'. She was interested in life around her, and made many appreciative comments about the welfare services she received: about the warden of the scheme where she lived, the Red Cross day centre which she attended and the outings they made to the seaside. One daughter lived outside London but came to see her every week. Her other daughter lived in the Midlands and telephoned regularly. She followed the careers of her grandchildren with great interest. She also received a number of regular visits from old friends and neighbours. The warden, and other tenants I talked to, spoke of her with great admiration, of how she bore her pains with great courage and did not complain.

She told me of the importance of religious faith in her life, but also that she disagreed with some of the things she had been taught as a child.

'... I believe implicitly that there is a life after this one, and I think it will be quite an adventure, and when it comes I shall be quite happy to go and meet all those that I knew and came along a bit before me. And it's helped a great deal too I think when things have gone rather bad—you know I've had quite a lot of pain in my life—and this knowledge has helped terrifically, you know, whereas if I hadn't had any faith I'm sure there would have been times when I would have got horribly miserable and fed up. But I think it's good if people can have some kind of faith, no matter what it is, so long as it's just something they can hang on to.'

'... I don't really think young people think a great deal about religion, and if they do, well, there's so many other things. I think it's later on in life that you begin to think more deeply about it and eventually accept one line or another, one faith or another. My oldest granddaughter is 16 and I don't think she has got many views on religion at the moment, but she probably will have later on.'

'... I was brought up in the Church of England but there are many things that they teach that I just can't accept ... I remember we were always taught when I was young that if a baby was born and not christened, it couldn't go to heaven. This I believed until we lost our own little one when he was very young, just a few weeks old, and the first thing I thought was, well he must be christened, and of course we sent for the vicar and he was in fact duly christened. But afterwards when I came to think, I thought well, what a ridiculous belief, what a thing to believe, that because a clergyman hasn't said a few words over a young lad, that child can't go to heaven, and it was those sorts of things that made me think ... as a matter of fact, the vicar himself, he passed that remark to my husband. He said, "Well I'm very glad you've had him christened because you know how important it is, he could never have entered the Kingdom of Heaven". And I thought I don't know, I don't think I can believe that now I come to think about it, and I certainly don't. But I think they have changed their views in quite a lot of things in the church today. There's another thing I've never been able to accept, the fact that Christ died on the cross, we were told that he takes all our sins, and that it doesn't matter how wicked you've been in life, as long as you say I'm sorry before you die all your sins are forgiven you. Well this I've never been able to accept. I think, I may be wrong, but I think that whatever mistakes we make here, that at some future date and some future life, we should be given the opportunity to put them right, and I think will have to put that right. I think we've got certain responsibilities, we are sent here in this life in preparation for the next.'

Her views on the modern world were tolerant. Although disliking certain trends, as the presentation of violence on television, and the loss of 'courtesy' in behaviour between the sexes, she disagreed with prejudice against the young. Each generation had to grow up in a different situation and that had to be taken into account.

'... there weren't the things to have and do when I was younger. We were perhaps more satisfied than the younger people are today, though no doubt if there were the opportunities then that there are now, we would have been exactly the same. I think it's the decade that you're brought up in that you live in, really ...'

'... it's a different life for women nowadays. I often wonder how so many young women manage to combine work and a home. I don't think, well I suppose I could have done, but I would have hated to have done it. When I was young I found a three bedroomed house and my husband and two children were quite enough for me to do, and I can honestly say that I was never bored. I could always find something to do. We used to make our own jams and pickles and things like that you know. Of course today there are so many more things to have, and everything is so expensive that I suppose the girl just thinks she's got to go out to work. And then things like holidays. Holidays were not generalized in my day, you were lucky if your husband had a job and you got a holiday with pay. But of course now it's possible to go abroad and all these things are very nice but of course they are all so expensive.'

She could see both sides of social change, for example the change in the appearance of the countryside.

'... the days when we could get out and walk a lot in the countryside before the advent of cars, that was a lovely time. I do go now on the rare occasions that my son-in-law takes me to the beauty spots, but the beauty of it for me is spoilt by so many cars and charabancs and that kind of thing, and I remember it of course when there wasn't, but this must be with progress, I mean I do realize that. More people can now enjoy it. It's just that when you've seen it, you know, as it used to be, it's not quite so good now, but as I say that's rather a selfish view, because so many more people now can enjoy these places.'

She had a firm belief in progress that was unusual in the people in this sample. She considered that most of the social changes she had experienced in her life time had been for the better.

Although she expressed a very positive attitude to thinking about the past, she did not speak about it a great deal to me, except in answers to direct questions. The warden also did not regard her as a 'reminiscer'. But memories, especially of her husband, were obviously very important to her. Like Mrs Parsons, she spoke now of seeing her life as a pattern.

'... when you stop to look back you realize how one thing has led to another, and it has sort of made a pattern. What do they say, "there's a divinity which shapes our ends"? I think there probably is.'

She said for example that she often wondered at the circumstances that had led to her meeting her husband. Her mother had encouraged her to apply for a job in a tobacconist's shop, which seemed very odd to her at the time. A customer had invited her one day to the theatre. At the time, she said, she was 'not really interested in men, only music'. She said she was busy that particular evening. He had changed the tickets for another evening. They had married within a year.

Mrs Manners was one of the most attractive people in my study. Her considerateness, for example, was demonstrated in the understanding she expressed for difficulties the warden faced in his job.

'... our particular warden has got too much work, he's not only got this building, but he's got one over the way as well, and he's expected to keep the place, corridors and that, clean. They are on call day and night if anybody is in trouble. Now I do feel that in this case it is too much, and you can tell at times that it gets him right down and he gets a lot of troubles and worries, you know I think it's too much for one man really. It wouldn't be so bad if they had somebody in to do the rough cleaning or if he had an electric scrubber or something like that to make the work easier. And he happens to be a very conscientious sort of man, you know he feels things intensely, and this worries him more than perhaps it would some other men. You know, some old people, can't help it I suppose, but they're inclined to be tactless at times, and they pass very hurtful remarks. Well where perhaps one man would perhaps shake his head or laugh it off, Mr Andrews can't, to him that's a personal thing you see, and he suffers because of it. Anyway, I've always found him very helpful, very kind really, and after living six years on my own I do appreciate it.'

In the course of the 1970s I saw Mrs Manners on two more occasions and she presented the same composed serene self. She had to enter hospital on a couple more occasions, in 1973 when the fitting in one knee broke and she had to go in for re-operation. In 1978 the fitting in the other knee broke, but as there was found to be too much bony destruction the surgeons stiffened the knee rather than replacing the joint. In 1981 and 1982 when she was 83 years old I spoke with her on four occasions, covering the same ground as ten years previously. She was now more disabled than before, and she received a regular home help to do her housework and shopping. There was also the problem that she was becoming anaemic as a result of the rheumatoid arthritis, but she could not tolerate iron medication. Her social world had remained the same. Her daughter came once a week, her friends visited regularly, and she was taken to the Red Cross Club every week.

Her attitudes to her life remained as positive as before. As to the past, she mentioned the same key elements that she had ten years earlier. She felt very satisfied. She said she reminisced somewhat less now. She had begun to reminisce a lot after her husband died and it had helped her a good deal then. But now she had less need. She did not think it good to 'live in the past'. In fact she answered, differently from ten years previously, that she now thought more about the future than the past, for example, about events in her family. As in 1971 she said her reminiscences concerned more her married years. Her morale remained high. She said she accepted what would be and did not worry, and was happy to go along as she was until she died. She still looked forward to things though, for example, her granddaughter's return from America. She did say that she had somewhat less pleasure in life than ten years previously, mainly because she could not play the piano as she used to. Nevertheless she tried to do what she could for herself. She still made cakes, and when I visited her she gave me tea. She expressed the same tolerant attitudes to society as before. If she had been born in the post-war period, she imagined that she would like pop music too.

'... one can't stop progress ... I'm not sure it's all good, but it's generally good.'

Although my talks with Mrs Manners over the years had established the stability of her high morale in the face of considerable pain and discomfort, and also indicated an important role for reminiscence in her adjustment to her husband's death, I had not really been able to gain much insight into how she had adjusted so remarkably well to the difficulties she had faced. It was only indeed in our very last meeting in 1982—which she was happy for me to tape record again—that I asked her directly for her own views on this.

I asked her in the first place what she thought was the secret of her happiness. She spoke of two factors, 'counting one's blessings' and 'keeping going'.

'... I think the real secret is with all the pain and operations and things I've had, I think I've always tried to count my blessings. I've always thought, well I've got my hearing and my sight and that means such a lot. I've got my music, and I've always done that. And people say sometimes, "How on earth do you keep so cheerful?". I say, "Well it's no good being miserable. You only make yourself miserable and everybody else". People don't want to know, do they.'

'... I still made myself keep about, even when the pain was awful. I thought, "Well if I sat down and say I can't do any more, then I've had it. And I'm not going to do it. I'm going to fight it." The doctor often laughs now when he comes in. He says, "Well, how are you?". I'll say, "Still fighting the wheelchair." He says, "Well if anyone's put up a fight, you have." Well it's the only way. The alternative was to sit down and say, "Well that's it, I can't do any more." That way, I would have gone up the wall.'

I suggested to her that this required a special strength. Did she, I ask, have an explanation for how she had that strength? Her answer was a religious one.

'... well I think it's been given to me from heaven. I know I am helped, but I believe very firmly in the afterlife and I believe our loved ones go on living and I believe that they help. I'm often conscious of them you know. And I know my husband is very often with me. Perhaps I'll suddenly remember something, a joke or something or other, and I can almost hear him laugh, you know. And that has helped me a lot, that faith and the knowledge that when I do pass they'll be there waiting for me. People might laugh, but that's my faith. And it's helped me go through all sorts of things.'

She then explained to me how her spiritualist beliefs had developed, after her first attendance at a seance when she was in her early forties and how she had been convinced by what she had heard. The medium had brought her in contact with her brother, who had been killed in the First World War, and he had spoken to her of her little boy.

'... she said, "He wants to talk direct to you". She said, "Just come and take my hands and I'll go into a trance and you talk to him". And I took her hands and he said, "Oh Win, thank God I've got through at last to you. I've been trying ever since I came over here ..." He said, "I've seen your little boy and he's growing up in spirit beautifully". He described him, he brought him back to me. Now nobody else in the place knew that. It was something I had never discussed. Because it happened years before ...'

I asked Mrs Manners why she had been so attracted to spiritualism in the first place. She said as a child she had had a tremendous fear of death and of God. Experiences of death had deeply shocked her, in particular the death of her brother. (She did not mention, but one can also think of, her real mother, who had died before she could remember.)

'... as a young girl I used to be terrified of death and I used to think "Whatever will I do when mother dies or dad dies". And really if I heard of anybody dying I used to say, "Mum, don't talk about it". I was so frightened of it ... I remember one of our neighbours died when I was 14 I was so horrified ...'

Although she had been brought up with a religious faith, she had been 'not too sure about the afterlife'. The invitation to attend a seance from a neighbour had come quite as a surprise though. She had always thought such a thing was 'terrible, the work of the devil'. But she was interested and she prayed beforehand.

'... I did send out prayers. "If there is anything in this spiritualism, let me have personal proof. But it must be personal proof"...'

Agan she saw a special coincidence that led her to the seance.

'...yes I can see the pattern now. I can see that although I was so much against believing in this—I couldn't accept it, I thought that anyone that believes in that must be bad—but

I realize now that I had got to believe in it. It was going to be given to me, and so gradually the pattern formed itself until I got the personal proof I asked for. But I would have never had accepted it unless I had. I thought, "No, I can't accept it. If there's anything in it, then please give me personal proof". And I had it. And I've accepted it.'

After this first experience she had attended services at the Spiritualist Church. Her husband had come too and been impressed by what he saw and heard. She had had a number of later experiences of the closeness of people who had died. Still she said, she had been hesitant to tell me.

'... that has helped me a great deal through life. But I don't know why I'm telling you this. I could never tell anybody else. Because I would expect them to say, "Oh I don't believe it". There's not many people do, you know. I mean I think it's wrong to force your ideas and opinions on anybody. If they're interested, yes, I'd be only too pleased ... but I do know that it's helped me through life, to keep going, keep cheerful and I'm quite sure I'd never gone through all the pain I've had if I hadn't had that faith ...'

'A most wonderful experience' she said had occurred just before I first met her, after her husband had died but before her first major operation. The warden's wife had come to her one morning in a state of excitement but also of embarrassment.

'... "Can I come in? I'm sorry about this. I had to come, but I'm afraid you'll think I'm barmy. I've had the most vivid dream. I've been so impressed and I must come and tell you about it. Don't think I'm mad. I've never had such a vivid dream in my life. I dreamed that I was standing out looking at the garden over there. I saw a tall gentleman." She described my husband to a "t". He used to wear a little enamel red cross—he belonged to the Red Cross Club—on his lapel. She described that lapel. She described his figure and she said he had a rose in his hand. "And I said to him, can I help you?" So he said, "Yes, you know Mrs Manners, don't you?" "Yes I do know her. She only lives over there." He said, "Yes I know". She said, "You'll have to wait if you knock because it takes her a long time to get to the door". He said, "Yes I know". But he said, "Will you please give her this rose? It's an Ena Harkness rose, and she'll understand". Now I was just about to go in and have an operation then, and I was having a pretty rough time. Now I think that was wonderful. The only way he could get through to me and say, "It's all right old girl, carry on, here's the rose". The Ena Harkness was his favourite rose. And I was so amazed. If she had known him it would have been another thing, but she didn't know him from Adam. I said, "Well you'll never know how much that message means to me". And it was another proof that he still does know, he still does understand. And it was at a time when I was going through an awful lot of pain, waiting to go in for an operation. But it bucked me up no end, that message did. She said, "I said to my husband"—because she didn't know whether I believed in the afterlife or anything—"well she'll think I'm mad" ... I sent out thoughts of thanks to him. It did, it bucked me up no end.'

For herself she had reconciled her spiritualist beliefs with the Anglican beliefs she had been brought up with.

'... I always have believed in God. And I think we get great help. I think if we pray and ask for help, it's given. In the same way as I think we all have our particular spirits. What is it the bible says, "For he shall give his angels charge concerning thee to keep thee in all thy ways". And I'm sure that there are these angels. "And they shall bear thee up in their hands, lest thou dash thy head against a stone." Well there you are, there's this spirit life ...'

Although she did 'not have much time for bishops and archbishops', she acknowledged the supremacy of Jesus Christ in the 'spirit life'.

She also told me of her very positive experiences of spiritual healing. In the first ten years of her illness, when the pain was at its greatest, she had gone with her husband to a healer in Surrey. The beneficial effect was immediate.

'... he took my toes one at a time, which were rigid. And there was a young fellow sitting in the corner of his room. And he said, "Come over here. I think you'll be interested here". He said, "Now this is a young doctor and he is very interested in our way of healing". And he said, "Now you see this lady's toes. They are rigid. What would you do?". So the doctor said he couldn't do anything. Only cut the tendons. So Mr Alfred said, "Well I'll show you what I do". And he just took—and normally I couldn't have borne anybody to touch me for the pain—he took one toe at a time and he gently moved it and finally he got them working until every toe had movement in it. He said, "Now I want you to keep on moving those toes. Don't stop". And then the ankles were stiff, rigid. He did the same with the ankles. He worked them round until there was movement. And he said, "Now promise me when you go home, you'll keep these exercises up ..." The hospital were amazed when I went back and they saw movement. They said, "Well you are a very lucky person. This is most unusual"...'

She still wrote for absent healing and believed it helped.

Her spiritual beliefs gave an extra meaning and vividness to her personal memories.

'... I shall welcome death because I know I shall then be with my husband. It's a funny thing, the thoughts you get. I used to meet him sometimes, when he worked in London. He'd say, "Come up to London, we'll go so and so". He always met me at the top of the escalator at Tottenham Court Road. It was a very big escalator. And even if I was early, he was always there first. And I like to think that when I pass he'll be there waiting. I've got that thought very prominently in my mind. As he used to be then. I used to say, "I'm early. How is it that you are here so soon?". "Oh well, I didn't want you waiting about." He'd always be there early, you know.'

Her husband had told her once, 'If I go before you, don't go clambering up to the cemetery with flowers. I shan't be there. I shall be where you are, in the living room. Put them in the home ...'

I did not have the opportunity to see Mrs Manners again. I heard from the warden later that she died twelve months after this conversation. She had been taken to hospital in a lot of pain and died a few days afterwards. The warden, who was a new one, said she did not know her well but that she was a 'lovely lady'.

It would be difficult to find someone so esteemed by all who knew her as Mrs Manners. In the twelve years that I knew her, despite increasing disability, her cheerfulness hardly wavered. Although she spoke a lot about death in her last conversation with me, she was not a gloomy person at all. Quite the opposite in fact. Her positive and optimistic attitudes to past, present and future remained essentially the same over the period of our conversations. Reminiscences of her happy life were important to her, and particularly at moments of difficulty, but she did not exaggerate them to the exclusion of the present, where also she said she had a lot to be thankful for, as when she referred to her daughter.

'... even now she comes up every week. I said to her, "Don't feel you have to come every week. It takes two hours to get here from there". And she said, "Mum, I'm coming every week". And she will, I know. I feel I'm so lucky and that's why I must keep going. Everybody has been good to me. I've got to do my bit. The thing is to count one's blessings in life.'

By broadcasting a happy personality she had attracted a lot of people to her.

But in drawing any conclusions on the reasons for her successful adjustment, one must take note of her own opinion that her happy attitudes were largely due to the fact that she had been helped to confront her fear of death in mid-life. She commented how death remained a hidden fear in many people's lives, 'swept under the carpet in the Western world'. 'In old age,' she said, 'life can be very hard if one cannot see beyond the grave.'

Chapter 10

Therapeutic Implications

Individual Differences and Variation

Evaluation studies on psychological and social work intervention have suffered from over-simplistic hypotheses. Whether a move to sheltered housing or provision of special domiciliary services 'is of greater benefit', or whether psychotherapy 'works' are the types of questions that are asked unfortunately all too often. The caring professions that have been educated in the social sciences have remained long in the shadow of the medical profession, but they have not yet learned some valuable lessons from the practice of medicine. In the investigation of the efficacy of a drug, for example, in influencing clearly diagnosed diseases, a much simpler type of situation than the ones faced by social work practitioners, questioning of practice nevertheless takes place at a relatively sophisticated level. What effects do different intensities of intervention have? Under what conditions and with what types of diseases? But few steps have been taken in the direction of finding such discriminating answers by researchers examining the efficacy of social care provision.

Human beings are not born all the same, and the varying circumstances of life make them increasingly diverse as they age. By the time they are old differences therefore are maximized. Needs and appropriate solutions differ considerably. But the practical emphasis of gerontological work in recent years has meant that we have learned more about different ways of providing services than we have about differences between people and their needs.

The same criticism applies to the original question with which the investigation on which this book is based began. Does reminiscence promote adjustment in late life? It should be long apparent that such a question is too naïve. We need rather to determine the conditions under which reminiscence is adaptive, and to relate such findings to our understanding of human personality. Memories in fact themselves provide an insight into individual differences. The psychoanalyst Alfred Adler for example laid great stress on the use of early memories in ascertaining the individual's fundamental view of life. It provides the therapist with a perspective in which to consider what type of help is required (Gilliland *et al.*, 1984).

The present study has not attempted to relate the use of reminiscence to a study of personality. But it has proposed a typology of attitudes to reminiscence, which can serve as an initial base at least for a more differentiated view of the value of reminiscence. Although crude, the validity of this typology is demonstrated by the longitudinal evidence that has been described, which indicates a very large degree of constancy of attitude to reminiscence over a period of ten years and more. In this time few people appeared to shift their major orientation to their memories of the past.

Having said that, such a typology is misleading if it is taken to imply exclusive categories. It describes themes which characterize some people more than others. But human beings are not invariable. At different times they can demonstrate diverse and even contrary characteristics. Some of the people in this study showed quite a variety of attitudes. The four orientations to reminiscence described in Chapters 5 to 8 therefore should be viewed as dynamic characteristics whose presence was felt at times more strongly and at other times negligibly in individuals' thoughts: taking possession of the past and treasuring it; struggling with guilt and regret and expressing sorrow; turning the mind to other tasks at hand; experiencing nostalgia and the pain of remembering what is lost. The attitudes of serenity and hope that characterized the people described in Chapter 9 were also not constant attributes of those who appeared nearest to a state of integrity. Even the most cheerful person knows at times what despair is.

The four types of attitudes to memories that have been delineated do, however, provide a starting point for considering the therapeutic use of reminiscence. In any initial diagnosis or assessment of an older person's situation, it seems to be well worthwhile noting the nature of the individual's reminiscence, the attitudes expressed to thinking and talking about the past, and whether the individual appears able to gain enjoyment from reminiscence. Negative attitudes to reminiscence are themselves revealing and take different forms. Before attempting an intervention, the worker should consider carefully what the likely benefit is going to be. He can choose to use or to avoid reminiscence as a means of working. The following comments are offered as points to be considered in making such a decision.

To Reminisce or Not To Reminisce

In those who already reminisce readily and have a positive attitude to memories of their past lives, these memories constitute strengths which can be tapped in the face of difficulties. But the links between past and present can be broken. The stresses and strains of old age may be so great that they disrupt the person's sense of continuity between past and present. Reminiscence then can come to seem irrelevant to the present situation. Thus, although reminiscence occurs naturally and spontaneously in many older people, there can be times when an outsider does need to promote it. For example, it may be the task for a social worker to remind a client that he or she has met crises before, has struggled and persevered. Such an interpretation of one's life history can serve as a powerful motivation to try and cope with the new demands of the present.

Of course a social worker may initially know little about the individual's past, but the very activity of exploring it together with the individual concerned will likely help them both to understand better the situation they are now in. At the least the client should feel that the social worker has a better appreciation of him/her as an individual. The social worker may be able to spot ways in which the individual has coped in the past which can be used again. Information collected also from others about the client's previous life may be useful to the social worker in challenging an older person's depressed view of himself and the world, and to help him reach a more positive view of his current efforts.

In this context it is interesting to note the findings from a comprehensive study of a community care scheme for elderly people that has been carried out by the University of Kent and Kent Social Services (Challis and Davies, 1985). This study has demonstrated that a flexible client centred scheme for providing support to frail individuals living in their own homes has marked advantages over relocation to residential care homes. Not only is it successful in preventing admission to institutional care at no greater cost to the public services, but it also appears to promote longer life and greater psychological well-being on the part of the recipients of the service. Among the indicators used for rating well-being, a measure of 'satisfaction with life progress' was included and this also showed up a significant difference between the two groups. The group receiving the special service had fewer regrets about their past lives. This raises the issue, already discussed in Chapter 4, of the relationship between present well-being and past life satisfaction. Why should providing a more sensitive service that allows people to stay in their own homes lead them to have a more positive view of their past?

Memory we know is coloured by present emotion. But this in itself seems insufficient to explain such a striking difference. Satisfaction with past life after all is a relatively stable characteristic (Gilleard et al., 1981), as the present study has also demonstrated. A more convincing explanation is that the greater satisfaction results from the greater interest taken in the individual's life by the social worker or other helpers concerned. It is clear from the Kent study that many more of the people receiving the special help to stay in their own homes also felt that they had someone in whom they could confide, and almost a half referred in this context to the social worker who had organized the help or one of the people who provided specific assistance. They indicated that an interest had been taken in them as persons, and this had helped them to maintain or regain a sense of self respect.

Moreover, it is not only that people may 'forget' about their own individual histories; they may also have adopted from society at large a general attitude to what has happened in the past as irrelevant, uninteresting or of no further value. Individuals in a group setting such as a long stay hospital or residential home may have done many worthwhile and interesting things in their lives, may have contributed to society in various ways, but need encouragement to come to re-evaluate these things—perhaps by the act of having to tell others about them. It is in such circumstances that the various forms of group reminiscence therapy, around particular themes and/or using visual and other aids (objects, pictures, slides...), are most helpful in stimulating memories and the sharing of experiences. A skilled leader is needed who can search beneath self effacing attitudes and elicit important memories, and not allow the more talkative and assertive individuals to dominate conversations. Fortunately the recent growth of interest in oral history has made the collection of reminiscences about past events and ways of life a truly valued contribution to society, and reminiscence work in a sheltered housing scheme or in an institutional setting can be given a similar status. This may have the double benefit of not only helping the individuals to value more their own memories, but also of encouraging the development of a sense of community based on shared experiences. More and more is now being written on the setting up of group reminiscence projects and the interested reader is referred to the work of Humphries (1984) and Bornat (1985) in the UK and Kaminsky (1984) in the USA.

But such creative reminiscing needs to be distinguished from a brooding on the past, such as was shown by people in the second group in the study I described. Their thoughts were often dominated by regretful memories about things they wished they had or had not done in their lives, or about sad things that had happened to them and their families. Short-term counselling offers a number of possibilities for helping such individuals. Again it is important to be clear about what one is dealing with. One needs for example to try and develop a sense of how justified or rational the person's accusations are. Especially if they are depressed, many individuals may have a tendency to blame themselves and feel guilty for past events for which they really had little or no personal responsibility. Also they may feel profoundly unlucky in a way which makes luck appear as something directed against them personally rather than a random occurrence.

Beck (1976) writes of the 'depressogenic error of generalization' whereby selective negative thinking is projected into the past. Various techniques have been suggested for countering such thinking by cognitive therapists; for example, 'disattribution' which involves teaching the client to stop attributing all blame to himself by recognizing the role played by fate and others in events (Rathjen *et al.*, 1978); or rational disputation of thoughts (Ellis, 1974) which encourages people to appreciate and then modify the way irrational beliefs about events often determine their feelings about things that happen to them; or by simply changing the forms of attention and seeing that there were positive things in the past as well as negative, and attending to them for a change. Some therapists specializing with older people, as Sherman (1981), regard such types of 'cognitive therapy' as being especially relevant to them. Circumstances in old age may not easily be changed, but it is possible to be more hopeful about changing a person's perception of them.

However, it would be very naïve to think that all problems with a difficult 'life review' can be solved in these ways. A person's sense of guilt may be well founded. As Sherman himself points out, where actual wrong has been done to someone and that person is dead, the wrong has to be accepted, not disputed. To do this would tend to make matters worse by making the client attest to his or her guilt all the more, as well as reducing confidence in the counsellor. One should listen to the client carefully, hear him out fully and completely, provide the necessary catharsis and then help to move him or her from a sense of guilt to a sense of forgiveness.

The importance of the help that can be provided by religious practices, as the Christian confession, is undeniable, and it is foolish of psychologists to ignore religious discussion of forgiveness, and also of the healing of tragic and hurtful memories (see Linn and Linn, 1974; MacNutt 1975). Jung is one of very few prominent psychologists who have openly acknowledged the psychological value of religion. It was vital, he held, for clergy and psychotherapists to join forces, and he was urging this more than 50 years ago (Jung, 1933). Indeed Jung was fond of saying that all of his patients had fallen ill because they had lost contact with their religious traditions, and that they recovered only in as much as they regained a religious outlook. Jung had a profound respect for the myths, symbols and rituals of religious tradition, seeing the symbol as a bridge between the conscious and the unconscious (Jung, 1934). Unfortunately a mutual antipathy between psychologists and religious thinkers has existed so long that psychotherapy and spiritual guidance are rarely discussed in the same context. But at last the beginning of a change of attitude is now evident on both sides (see for example Leech, 1977; Bergin, 1983). Christian practice, it should be noted, stresses sorrow and forgiveness, not guilt.

The life review as described by Butler and later writers (for example Kaminsky, 1984) should be seen as a natural activity, perhaps especially but not exclusively related to old age (see Webster and Young, 1986; Molinari and Reichlin, 1985), and one that needs our respect. We would benefit from more descriptive material on the courses life reviews can take. A number of individuals in this study had seemed to have been through such a process, and it is important to stress that people do not necessarily want or benefit from the help of a counsellor in 'putting their house in order'. For some indeed it may be an entirely private matter. But for those with deep feelings of regret and dissatisfaction it may be vital that they are not left alone with their thoughts. Creative use can also be made of negative reminiscences, and writing an autobiography for a small group of interested others or for a therapist is better than sitting around and brooding about past events. The poems of Thomas Hardy written after the death of his wife in the course of 1912–13 are the fruit of his own remorse and regret about the unsatisfactory way their marriage had developed. They are universally recognized to be the peak of his literary achievement.

It must also be admitted, however, that there is some danger of over emphasizing intrapsychic aspects in discussing the situation of older people. Neither psychology—nor religion for that matter—concerns itself only with what happens within the individual. Each person has a need to be connected with the world at large, and a crucial problem of old age, apparent especially in modern western societies, is the isolation and loss of role and purpose in society which many old people can feel. The former supports and expressive outlets in family and at work which people have relied on to maintain adjustment may be gone. Of all the classical psychotherapists Alfred Adler has perhaps the most to say about loss of self esteem in old age (Adler, 1956). Feelings of uselessness or inferiority present the individual with a challenge to overcome from childhood onwards, and the key for Adler is the acquisition of 'Gemeinschaftsgefühl', usually translated as 'social interest', i.e. taking into account the well-being of other people.

Many negative phenomena in old age, as hypochondriasis and prejudiced views, may reflect fears about loss of identity and inferiority. Bringing a person to a less egocentric view of life, and to develop interest in the happiness of others, may be the best way of combatting such feelings. Therefore rather than staying with the individual in his morbid thoughts about the past, it may be much more profitable to try to encourage an orientation to the world around him, to develop social interests and contacts. Again it must be stressed, judgement is required as to whether reminiscence is a productive or counter productive activity, and whether some other intervention might be called for.

In those who deny the importance of reminiscence to them—the third group in this study—we should not lightly dismiss their view as (over) defensive. Most of the people I interviewed who came into this category had very understandable reasons for not reminiscing. They were too busy with other things they preferred to do. Some had been provided with opportunities they had not had earlier in life and wanted to make the most of them. If help does need to be offered to such people it surely makes more sense to help them to continue with their chosen way of life and special interests—find ways of transporting them to their old clubs, for example, or provide special aids to compensate for disabilities—rather than to say that they should sit quietly and contemplate their past. Some too, especially perhaps the very old members of society, may well have been through a period of life review and feel no need to retrace their steps. Sufficient for them the issues of the day.

There were a few people in my study who seemed to be actively resisting thinking about unhappy aspects of their past lives. But this too may be a strength which needs to be respected, a defence against thoughts which the individual senses he is unable to handle. Probing of such 'defences' needs to be done warily, for it may be easier to do damage than to repair it again.

The final group, it will be remembered, were those who tried not to reminisce although they said that their past lives had been very happy. The reason for their avoidance was because, they said, it was too painful to reminisce. It made them more sad than they need be. All these people were, when I first spoke to them, or subsequently became, depressed. All had been bereaved or had suffered another important loss (for example, severe disability or separation from a previously close family) and had not come to terms with these changes. In retrospect it seemed evident that the avoidance of reminiscence had reflected their inability to overcome these losses, and perhaps resulted from their failure to grieve satisfactorily. The link between reminiscence and grieving has already been raised in Chapter 8. In those who never give up wishing for the return of the past, reminiscence may not be pleasurable because they are unable to detach themselves from and freely enjoy their memories of the past, as memories. One can speculate on the influence of experiences in childhood, where the ability to tolerate the substitution of a satisfying memory for the missing 'love object' normally develops.

But it seems likely that this outcome occurs most where people have become very dependent on past relationships and roles for their idea of themselves. Worden views highly dependent relationships as especially difficult to grieve (Worden, 1982). He cites the research of Horowitz and colleagues in San Francisco who suggest that a person who has a highly dependent relationship and then loses the source of that dependency experiences 'a change in self-image from that of a strong person, well sustained by the relationship with a strong other, to the pre-existent structure of a weak, helpless waif supplicating in vain for rescue by a lost or abandoning person' (Horowitz *et al.*, 1980).

Among the particular people I interviewed this may well have been an important factor. The three men who had all been bereaved gave indications of having lived very much for their wives. The three women who came into this category had, because of relocation or disability, lost the close links with family and friends and colleagues in a voluntary welfare organization that had been the focus of their lives. At the least it seems plausible to suggest that persistent inhibited or painful reminiscence, of the kind these people showed, is a good indicator of the need for grief therapy.

A proper consideration of reminiscence raises many other issues of importance in old age, and it therefore seems right that increasing attention is being given to it. My main point, however, has been to emphasize that one cannot make simple generalizations about the value of reminiscence. Each person needs to be considered in a special way. Whether reminiscence is a positive or negative factor in their lives, whether they can be helped with reminiscence which disturbs them or causes them pain, whether reminiscence should be avoided or stimulated, are all questions which call for a careful appraisal. Certainly memories can be a source of great creativity, and this is an important point to stress, but older people should be offered many other possibilities as well to express themselves. Research on the value of formally stimulated reminiscence—for example, in institutional settings—should take a differential view, paying due attention to each individual's life history and circumstances.

Reminiscence and Mental Deterioration

The previous view that reminiscence was related to or even caused mental deterioration has been turned on its head. Now reminiscence is seen as the 'new' means of preserving mental functioning in old age. A number of recent papers have pointed to the benefits of organized reminiscence in psychogeriatric institutions both to patients and staff (Kiernat, 1979; Lesser *et al.*, 1981; Norris and Abu El Eileh, 1982; Cook, 1984). Although most of the evidence is of an anecdotal nature rather than quantitative, it is consistently positive. The writers point to improvements as increased participation in discussion and more spontaneity on the part of the people involved (stressed both by Cook and by Norris and Abu El Eileh), greater socialization before and after the sessions, even higher self esteem and behavioural improvements.

The nurses and other staff involved have been said to benefit from knowing the older people better and as a result being able to form closer relationships with them. Other valuable spin-offs are referred to (for example, the formation of activity programmes based on the interests expressed in the groups). Evidence has also been collected that structured reminiscence exercise leads to improvement in cognitive functioning as measured by the Raven Standard Progressive Matrices (Hughston, 1976). At the least, activities involving reminiscence seem to be a very suitable means of attracting and maintaining the engagement of many older people.

Comparison with the enthusiasm expressed for reality orientation comes readily to mind. As Woods and Britton point out in their recent text on *Clinical Psychology with the Elderly* (Woods and Britton, 1985), research on the benefits of reminiscence in institutions for the old will now probably mushroom and researchers should take note of the lessons emerging from the previous research on reality orientation.

However, there is some danger that this association will lead, at least as far as mentally deteriorated people are concerned, to an exclusive concern with the 'cognitive' and 'activity' benefits of reminiscence therapy, and a neglect of the broader issues of the relationship between reminiscence and psychological adjustment that have been the focus of this book. Yet these same issues, such as maintenance of identity, present themselves as much with people suffering from dementia as with other older people, perhaps even more so. For example, we often need to look beyond the immediate content of the reminiscence towards its meaning for the person. Reminiscence may be a means of communicating feelings which if expressed directly would be difficult to handle both for the individuals concerned and the people who care for them. One illustration of this is talk about parents. Older people, and older women in particular, do seem to reminisce a lot about childhood. But why do confused old people speak so often about their parents as if they were alive? Does this tell us something about their sense of security and need for roots (Miesen, 1985)?

The case of Mrs Tucker presented in Chapter 8 illustrates the continuity in an individual's concerns despite mental deterioration and placement with others labelled as 'elderly mentally infirm'. She was still the same person, the meaning of her reminiscences still understandable to someone who had known her before. In recognizing reminiscence as a valuable activity for mentally deteriorated older people, we should not thereby become insensitive to what is said. Nor should we assume that reminiscence activities will suit everyone equally.

Epilogue

It is with a sense of individual difference and variation in old age that I would like to close this book. I hope that I have demonstrated that the attitudes to reminiscence displayed by older people are worth close consideration by those in the helping professions. Disturbed memories need to be faced. Care has to be exercised though in judging whether self accusatory memories are the symptoms of a depression that require challenging, or whether they call out instead for healing and a genuine reconciliation with people from the past. A flight from happy memories also seems to be a sign of the need for therapy, an indication of an incomplete grieving process. Memories for many people will be a treasure, a solace and a source of wonder. What we can do to strengthen bonds between the past and the present, and preserve a sense of continuity for people who are threatened by loss, will be appreciated.

But memories will not have this special aura for everyone. For some the past is genuinely over. Experiences positive and negative have been fully assimilated. A state of serenity and inner peace has been reached, living in the present and just 'being' are now the goals. Others will be more orientated to the present because their current life situation invites them to be so involved. For others still this will be a natural preference.

It is true that some people put a very high value on memories as their most treasured possessions. For others the past is gone and unimportant. The development of such a value orientation deserves analysis in its own right. At which point in the lifespan does it emerge, and how stable is it over time? It should be noted that the value an individual places on his or her memories of past experience is different from being satisfied with one's past life. It is also different from the affective quality of one's memories. It is rather an evaluation of the importance of memories to the individual as a personal possession. Presumably we all value our personal memories to some degree as a bedrock of personal identity, but some put more value on them than others.

References

Abrams, M. (1978). *Beyond Three-Score and Ten. A First Report on a Survey of the Elderly*, Age Concern England, Mitcham, Surrey.

Adler, A. (1956). *The Individual Psychology of Alfred Adler*, edited by Ansbacher, H.L., and Ansbacher, R.R., Harper & Row, New York.

Antonovsky, A. (1979). *Health, Stress and Coping*, Jossey-Bass, London.

Austin, J.L. (1962). *How To Do Things With Words* (The William James Lectures delivered at Harvard University in 1955), edited by Urmson, J.O., Oxford University Press, London.

Beck, A.T. (1976). *Cognitive Therapy and the Emotional Disorders*, International Universities Press, New York.

Becker, H.S. (1963). *Outsiders: Studies in the Sociology of Deviance*, Free Press, New York.

Bergin, A.E. (1983). 'Religiosity and mental health: a critical re-evaluation and meta-analysis', *Professional Psychology: Research and Practice*, **14**, 170–184.

Bigot, A. (1974). 'The relevance of American life satisfaction indices for research on British subjects before and after retirement', *Age and Ageing*, **3**, 113–121.

Blum, J.E., and Tross, S. (1980). 'Psychodynamic treatment of the elderly: a review of issues in theory and practice', in Eisdorfer, C. (ed.), *Annual Review of Gerontology and Geriatrics*, **1**, 204–234.

Blythe, R. (1979). *The View in Winter: Reflections on Old Age*, Allen Lane, Harmondsworth, London.

Boldy, D., Abel, P., and Carter, K. (1973). *The Elderly in Grouped Dwellings. A Profile*, The Institute of Biometry and Community Medicine, University of Exeter.

Bornat, J. (1985). 'Exploring living memory—the uses of reminiscence', *Ageing and Society*, **5**, 333–337.

Bromley, D.B. (1978). 'Approaches to the study of personality changes in adult life and old age', in Isaacs, A.D., and Post, F. (eds.), *Studies in Geriatric Psychiatry*, John Wiley & Sons, Chichester.

Bromley, D.B. (1986). *The Case-study Method in Psychology and Related Disciplines*, John Wiley & Sons, Chichester.

Bühler, C. (1933). *Der Menschliche Lebenslauf als Psychologisches Problem*, 2nd edition (1959), Verlag für Psychologie, Göttingen.

Busse, E.W. (1985). 'Normal ageing: the Duke longitudinal studies', in Bergener, M., Ermini, M., and Stahelin, H.B., (eds.), *Thresholds in Aging*, Academic Press, New York, 215–229.

Butler, A., Oldman, C., and Greve, J. (1983). *Sheltered Housing for the Elderly: Policy, Practice and the Consumer*, George Allen & Unwin, London.

Butler, R.N. (1963). 'The Life Review: an interpretation of reminiscence in the aged', *Psychiatry*, **26**, 65–76.

Butler, R.N., and Lewis, M.I. (1977). *Aging and Mental Health*, C.V. Mosby & Co., St. Louis.

Campbell, A., Converse, P.E., and Rodgers, W.L. (1976). *The Quality of American Life*, Russell Sage Foundation, New York.

Carlson, C.M. (1984). 'Reminiscing: toward achieving ego integrity in old age', *Social Casework: The Journal of Contemporary Social Work*, **February 1984**, 81–89.

Castelnuovo-Tedesco, P. (1978). 'The mind as a stage: some comments on reminiscence and internal objects', *International Journal of Psychoanalysis*, **59**, 19–25.

Castelnuovo-Tedesco, P. (1980). 'Reminiscence and nostalgia: the pleasure and pain of remembering', in Greenspan, S.I., and Pollack, G.H. (eds.), *The Course of Life: Psychoanalytic Contributions toward Understanding Personality Development, Volume III: Adulthood and the Aging Process*, US Department of Health and Human Services, Washington DC, 115–127.

Cattell, R. B., and Eber, H. W. (1966). *The Sixteen Personality Factor Questionnaire Test*, Institute for Personality and Ability Testing, Champaign, Illinois.

Challis, D., and Davies, B. (1985). *Community Care for the Frail Elderly*, Report for the Department of Health and Social Security, Personal Social Services Research Unit, University of Kent.

Chown, S.M. (1977). 'Morale, careers and personal potentials', in Birren, J.E., and Schaie, K.W. (eds.), *Handbook of the Psychology of Aging*, Van Nostrand Reinhold, New York, 672–691.

Clayton, V. (1975). 'Erikson's theory of human development as it applies to the aged: wisdom as contradictive cognition', *Human Development*, **18**, 119–128.

Coleman, P.G. (1972). *The Role of the Past in Adaptation to Old Age*. PhD thesis, University of London.

Coleman, P.G. (1974). 'Measuring reminiscence characteristics from conversation as adaptive features of old age', *International Journal of Aging and Human Development*, **5**, 281–294.

Coleman, P.G. (1983). *The Past in the Present. A Report of Studies on the Adaptive Value of Reminiscence and Attitude to Past Life in Old Age*. Report, University of Southampton.

Coleman, P.G. (1984). 'Assessing self-esteem and its sources in elderly people', *Ageing and Society*, **4**, 117–135.

Coleman, P.G., and McCulloch, A.W. (1985). 'The study of psychosocial change in late life: some conceptual and methodological issues', in Munnichs, J.M.A., Mussen, P., Olbrich, E., and Coleman, P.G. (eds.), *Life-Span and Change in a Gerontological Perspective*, Academic Press, New York, 239–255.

Cook, J.B. (1984). 'Reminiscing: how it can help confused nursing home residents', *Social Casework: The Journal of Contemporary Social Work*, **February 1984**, 90–93.

Cowgill, D.O., and Holmes, L. (eds.) (1972). *Aging and Modernization*, Appleton-Century-Crofts, New York.

Cowgill, D.O. (1984). 'The disengagement of an aging activist: the making and unmaking of a gerontologist', in Spicker, S.F., and Ingman, S.R. (eds.), *Vitalizing Long-term Care*, Springer Publishing Company, New York, 221–228.

Cumming, E., and Henry, W. (1961). *Growing Old: The Process of Disengagement*, Basic Books, New York.

Dempsey, P. (1964). 'A undimensional depression scale for the MMPI', *Journal of Consulting Psychology*, 28, 364–370.

Dobrof, R. (1984). 'Introduction: a time for reclaiming the past', in Kaminsky, M. (ed.), *The Uses of Reminiscence: New Ways of Working with Older Adults*, The Haworth Press, New York.

Ellis, A. (1974). *Humanistic Psychotherapy: The Rational-Emotive Approach*, McGraw-Hill, New York.

Erikson, E. (1950). *Childhood and Society*, Norton, New York, republished (1965), Penguin, Harmondsworth, London.

Erikson, E. (1978). 'Reflections on Dr Borg's Life Cycle', in Erikson, E. (ed.), *Adulthood*, W.W. Norton, New York.

Festinger, L. (1957). *A Theory of Cognitive Dissonance*, Stanford University Press, Stanford.

Fischer, D.H. (1978). *Growing Old in America*, Oxford University Press, New York and Oxford.

Frankl, V.E. (1963). *Man's Search for Meaning: An Introduction to Logotherapy*, Pocket Books, New York.

Gendlin, E.T. (1962). *Experiencing and the Creation of Meaning*, Free Press, New York.

Gendlin, E.T. (1981). *Focusing* (2nd edition), Bantam Books, New York.

Gilleard, C.J., Willmott, M., and Vaddadi, K.S. (1981). 'Self report measures of mood and morale in elderly depression', *British Journal of Psychiatry*, **138**, 220–235.

Gilliland, B.E., James, R.K., Roberts, G.T., and Bowman, J.T. (1984). *Theories and Strategies in Counseling and Psychotherapy*, Prentice-Hall, Englewood Cliffs, New Jersey.

Goffman, E. (1959). 'The moral career of the mental patient', *Psychiatry*, **22**, 2–20.

Gottschalk, L.A., Gleser, G.C., and Springer, K.J. (1961). 'An anxiety scale applicable to verbal samples', *Archives of General Psychiatry*, **5**, 593–605.

Gottschalk, L.A., Gleser, G.C., and Springer, K.J. (1963). 'Three hostility scales applicable to verbal samples', *Archives of General Psychiatry*, **9**, 254–279.

Gurland, B.J., and Toner, J.A. (1982). 'Depression in the elderly: a review of recently published studies', in Eisdorfer, C. (ed.), *Annual Review of Gerontology and Geriatrics*, **3**, 228–265.

Hareven, T.K., and Adams, K.J. (eds.) (1982). *Aging and Life Course Transitions: An Interdisciplinary Perspective*, Tavistock Publications, London.

Harris, L. *et al.* (1975). *The Myth and Reality of Aging in America*, National Council on the Aging, Washington DC.

Havighurst, R.J. (1959). 'Social and psychological needs of the aging', in Gorlow, L., and Katkovsky, W. (eds.), *Readings in the Psychology of Adjustment*, McGraw-Hill, New York.

Havighurst, R.J., and Glasser, R. (1972). 'An exploratory study of reminiscence', *Journal of Gerontology*, **27**, 235–253.

Help the Aged, (1981). *Recall: A Handbook*, Help the Aged Education Department, London.

Horowitz, M.J., *et al.* (1980). 'Pathological grief and the activation of latent self-images', *American Journal of Psychiatry*, **137**, 1157–1162.

Hughston, G.A. (1976). *The Effects of Two Educational Interventions on the Cognitive Functioning of Older People*, Doctoral dissertation, Pennsylvania State University, University Park, Pa 37 (5).

Humphries, S. (1984). *The Handbook of Oral History: Recording Life Stories*, Inter-Action Imprint, London.

Johnson, M.L. (1976). 'That was your life: a biographical approach to later life', in Munnichs, J.M.A., and van den Heuvel, W.J.A. (eds.), *Dependency and Interdependency in Old Age*, Martinus Nijhoff, The Hague, 147–161.

Jung, C.G. (1933). *Modern Man in Search of a Soul*, Routledge and Kegan Paul, London.

Jung, C.G. (1934). *The Integration of the Personality*, Routledge and Kegan Paul, London.

Kaminsky, M. (1984). 'Transfiguring life: images of continuity hidden among the fragments', in Kaminsky, M. (ed.), *The Uses of Reminiscence. New Ways of Working with Older Adults*, The Haworth Press, New York.

Kiernat, J.M. (1979). 'The use of life review activity with confused nursing home residents', *American Journal of Occupational Therapy*, **33**, 306–310.

Krasner, J. (1977). 'Treatment of the elder person', in Fabrikant, B., Barron, J., and Krasner, J. (eds.). *To Enjoy is to Live*, Nelson Hall, Chicago.

Kurtz, I. (1983). *Loneliness*, Basil Blackwell, Oxford.

Langer, E.J. (1983). *The Psychology of Control*, Sage Publications, Beverly Hills.

Lawton, M.P. (1984). 'The varieties of wellbeing', in Malatesta, C.Z., and Izard, C.E., (eds.), *Emotion in Adult Development*, Sage Publications, Beverly Hills, 67–84.

Leech, K. (1977). *Soul Friend. A Study of Spirituality*, Sheldon Press, London.

Lesser, J., Lazarus, L.W., Frankel, J., and Havasy, S. (1981). 'Reminiscence group therapy with psychotic geriatric inpatients', *The Gerontologist*, **21**, 291–296.

Levinson, D. (1978). *The Seasons of a Man's Life*, Knopf, New York.

Lewis, C.N. (1971). 'Reminiscing and self-concept in old age', *Journal of Gerontology*, **26**, 240–243.

Lewis, C.N. (1973). 'The adaptive value of reminiscing in old age', *Journal of Geriatric Psychiatry*, **6**, 117–121.

Lidz, T. (1968). *The Person: His Development throughout the Life Cycle*, Basic Books, New York.

Lieberman, M.A., and Falk, J.M. (1971). 'The remembered past as a source of data for research on the life cycle', *Human Development*, **14**, 132–141.

Lieberman, M.A., and Tobin, S.S. (1983). *The Experience of Old Age. Stress, Coping and Survival*, Basic Books, New York.

Linn, D., and Linn, M. (1974). *Healing of Memories*, Paulist Press, New York.

Maas, H.S., and Kuyper, J.A. (1977). *Fromt Thirty to Seventy*, Jossey-Bass, San Francisco.

MacNutt, F. (1975). *Healing*, Bantam Books, New York.

Maugham, S. (1959). Cited by Butler (1963).

McCulloch, A.W. (1985). *Adjustment to Old Age in a Changing Society*. Ph.D. thesis, University of Southampton.

McMahon, A.W., and Rhudick, P.J. (1964). 'Reminiscing: adaptational significance in the aged', *Archives of General Psychiatry*, **10**, 292–298, republished in Levin, S., and Kahana, R. J. (eds.) (1967), *Psychodynamic Studies on Aging. Creativity, Reminiscing and Dying*, International Universities Press, New York.

Merriam, S. (1980). 'The concept and function of reminiscence: a review of the research', *The Gerontologist*, **20**, 604–609.

Merriam, S., and Cross, L. (1982). 'Adulthood and reminiscence: a descriptive study', *Educational Gerontology*, **8**, 275–290.

Miesen, B. (1985). 'Meaning and function of the remembered parents in normal and abnormal old age', paper presented at the *XIIIth International Congress of Gerontology*, New York.

Molinari, V., and Reichlin, R.E. (1985). 'Life review reminiscence in the elderly: a review of the literature', *International Journal of Aging and Human Development*, **20**, 81–92.

Morris, C.W. (1946). *Signs, Language and Behavior*, Prentice-Hall, New York.

Munnichs, J.M.A. (1966). *Old Age and Finitude*, Karger, Basle.

Munnichs, J.M.A., Mussen, P., Olbrich, E., and Coleman, P.G. (eds.), (1985), *Lifespan and Change in a Gerontological Perspective*, Academic Press, New York.

Murphy, E. (1982). 'Social origins of depression in old age', *British Journal of Psychiatry*, **141**, 135–142.

Neisser, U. (1982). *Memory Observed. Remembering in Natural Contexts*, W.H. Freeman and Company, San Francisco.

Neugarten, B. L., Havighurst, R. J., and Tobin, S. S. (1961). 'The measurement of life satisfaction', *Journal of Gerontology*, **16**, 134–143.

Neugarten, B.L., *et al.* (1964). *Personality in Middle and Later Life*, Atherton Press, New York.

Norris, A.D., and Abu El Eileh, M.T. (1982). 'Reminiscence groups', *Nursing Times*, **78**, 1368–1369.

Orwell, G. (1939). *Coming up for Air*, Gollancz, London.

Pear, T.H. (1922). *Remembering and Forgetting*, Methuen, London.

Pollack, G.H. (1981). 'Reminiscence and insight', *Psychoanalytic Study of the Child*, **36**, 279–287.

Rabbitt, P. (1984). 'Investigating the Grey Areas', *Times Higher Education Supplement*, **June 1, 1984**, 14.

Rathjen, D.P., Rathjen, E.D., and Hiniker, A. (1978). 'A cognitive analysis of social performance', in Foreyt, J.P., and Rathjen, D.P. (eds.), *Cognitive Behavior Therapy: Research and Application*, Plenum Press, New York.

Rosenmayr, L. (1981). 'Objective and subjective perspectives of life span research', *Ageing and Society*, **1**, 29–49.

Rosow, I., and Breslau, N. (1966). 'A Guttman health scale for the aged', *Journal of Gerontology*, **21**, 556–559.

Salaman, E. (1970). *A Collection of Moments: A Study of Involuntary Memories*, Longman, London.

Schachtel, E.G. (1959). *Metamorphosis*, Basic Books, New York.

Schaie, K.W. (1970). 'A reinterpretation of age related changes in cognitive structure and functioning', in Goulet, L.R., and Baltes, P.B. (eds.), *Life Span Developmental Psychology. Research and Theory*, Academic Press, New York, 485–507.

Seabrook, J. (1980). *The Way We Are*, Age Concern England, Mitcham, Surrey.

Sherman, E. (1981). *Counseling the Aging. An Integrative Approach*, The Free Press, New York.

Sherman, E. (1984). *Working with Older Persons. Cognitive and Phenomenological Methods*, Kluwer Nijhoff, Boston and The Hague.

Soskin, W.F., and John, V.P. (1963). 'The study of spontaneous talk', in Barker, R.G. (ed.), *The Stream of Behavior*, Appleton Century Crofts, New York, 228–281.

Stott, M. (1981). *Ageing for Beginners*, Basil Blackwell, Oxford.

Taylor, R. and Ford, G. (1981). 'Lifestyle and ageing. Three traditions in lifestyle research, *Ageing and Society*, **1**, 329–345.

Thomae, H. (ed.) (1976). *Patterns of Aging*, Karger, Basle.

Thomas, W., and Znaniecki, F. (1918–20) (1966). *The Polish Peasant in Europe and America. Monograph of an Immigrant Group* (5 vols), The Gorham Press, Boston, Massachusetts.

Thompson, P. (1978). *The Voice of the Past: Oral History*, Oxford University Press, Oxford.

Tinker, A. (1984). *Staying at Home: Helping Elderly People*, Her Majesty's Stationery Office, London.

Tobin, S.S., and Etigson, E. (1968). 'Effects of stress on earliest memory', *Archives of General Psychiatry*, **19**, 435–444.

Townsend, P. (1957). *The Family Life of Old People*, Routledge and Kegan Paul, London.

Townsend, P. (1962). *The Last Refuge*, Routledge and Kegan Paul, London.

Tunstall, J. (1966). *Old and Alone*, Routledge and Kegan Paul, London.

Webster, J.D., and Young, R.A. (1986). 'Process variables of the life review: counseling implications, *International Journal of Aging and Human Development* (in press).

Wheeler, R. (1982). 'Staying put: a new development in policy?'. *Ageing and Society*, **2**, 299–329.

Williams, R.H., and Wirths, C.G. (1965). *Lives Through the Years*, Aldine-Atherton, Chicago.

Woods, R.T., and Britton, P.G. (1985). *Clinical Psychology with the Elderly*, Croom Helm, London.

Worden, J.W. (1982). *Grief Counseling and Grief Therapy*, Springer, New York.

Zinberg, N., and Kaufman, I. (1963). 'Cultural and personality factors associated with aging: an introduction', in Zinberg, N. and Kaufman, I. (eds.), *Normal Psychology of the Aging Process*, International Universities Press, New York.

Suggested Further Reading on Reminiscence

For an interesting collection of new and not so new psychological perspectives on the role of memory in our lives Ulric Neisser's *Memory Observed* is highly recommended.

Neisser, U. (1982). *Memory Observed. Remembering in Natural Contexts*, W.H. Freeman and Company, San Franciso.

In regard to the function of reminiscence in the lives of older people, the thorough account by Morton Lieberman and Sheldon Tobin of many years' research at the University of Chicago on the adjustment of people being moved into institutional settings, gives considerable attention to the role of reminiscence and is essential reading for students of the subject.

Lieberman, M.A., and Tobin, S.S. (1983) *The Experience of Old Age. Stress, Coping and Survival*, Basic Books, New York.

Edmund Sherman's recent book on *Working with Older Persons* gives fresh insight into the place of reminiscence in psychotherapy.

Sherman, E. (1984). *Working with Older Persons. Cognitive and Phenomenological Methods*, Kluwer Nijhoff, Boston and The Hague.

Still valuable reading is the general account of mental health work with older people by Robert Butler and Myrna Lewis, which includes Butler's thinking on the 'life review'.

Butler, R.N., and Lewis, M.I. (1977). *Aging and Mental Health*, C.V. Mosby and Company, St Louis (3rd edition, 1982).

For clinical psychologists, Robert Woods and Peter Britton provide a useful introduction to the beginnings of evaluative work on reminiscence therapy in institutional settings.

Woods, R.T., and Britton, P.G. (1985). *Clinical Psychology with the Elderly*, Croom Helm, London.

There is now a flourishing interchange between oral history and reminiscence therapy. A classic account of the rise of oral history is provided by Paul Thompson.

Thompson, P. (1978). *The Voice of the Past: Oral History*, Oxford University Press, Oxford.

A more recent account of methods in oral history is:

Humphries, S. (1984). *The Handbook of Oral History: Recording Life Stories*, Inter-Action Imprint, London.

A delightful collection on *The Uses of Reminiscence*, both therapeutic and artistic, is:

Kaminsky, M. (ed.) (1984). *The Uses of Reminiscence: New Ways of Working with Older Adults*, The Haworth Press, New York.

One should also not neglect the broader multi-disciplinary context in which life history is being studied. A noteworthy recent collection, edited by a historian and by an anthropologist, is:

Hareven, T.K., and Adams, K.J. (eds.) (1982). *Aging and Life Course Transitions: An Interdisciplinary Perspective*, Tavistock Publications, London.

The two following books provide a more sociological, comparative and methodological context for the study of individual life-histories.

Bertaux, D. (ed.) (1981). *Biography and Society: The Life History Approach in the Social Sciences*, Sage, Beverly Hills.

Plummer, K. (1983). *Documents of Life: An Introduction to the Problems and Literature of a Humanistic Method*, George Allen & Unwin, London.

Author Index

Subject Index